THE CARELESS ATOM

THE

CARELESS

ATOM

by

SHELDON NOVICK

HOUGHTON MIFFLIN COMPANY
BOSTON
1969

Library of Congress Catalog Card Number:
68–9768

This book is for Sherwood

There is an understandable drive
on the part of men of good will
to build up the positive aspects of nuclear energy
simply because the negative aspects
are so distressing.

Dr. Alvin Weinberg
Director, Oak Ridge National
Laboratory (1956)

ACKNOWLEDGMENTS

IT WOULD BE DIFFICULT to acknowledge my full indebtedness to Dr. Barry Commoner without saddling him with responsibility for any errors or failings in what follows. For the past four years I have been his student as well as his assistant, and what little I know about the tangled relationship between science and society I learned from him. Those of my readers who are acquainted with his work will easily see the great debt which this book owes him.

Another debt is owed to the Committee for Environmental Information, which in a direct way made this book, and many other more important enterprises like it, possible.

It was an article by Lin Mattison and Richard Daly which first drew my interest to reactors, and many of the ideas presented here were first suggested in long discussions with Lin. to whom I am also grateful for access to his extensive files.

Special thanks are due to David Pesonen, who started it all. I am indebted to his writings, more of which I hope will soon be published, as well as to our conversations, particularly for much of the material in Chapter III.

Linda Mattison's comments, corrections, and suggestions came at a time when they were much needed, and appreciated.

Professor Harold Green was kind enough to read the manu-

script and to make a number of useful corrections and suggestions. For these, and his kind encouragement on other occasions, I am deeply grateful.

I particularly want to thank Dr. Bernard Spinrad for his
kindness and courtesy in commenting on the manuscript before
publication.

Miss Eva Schneider was of very great assistance in the prep-
aration of early drafts of the manuscript, often under trying
circumstances. My thanks are also very much due to Miss
Lenore Harris, whose help through all stages of this project
was invaluable. Miss Joy Wolfe and Mrs. Elayne Drey were
also of assistance in typing.

None of the kind people mentioned here are to be held responsible for any of the statements which follow, nor for any
errors which they may have been unable to keep me from
making.

SHELDON NOVICK

CONTENTS

THE CARELESS ATOM

I

ACCIDENTS HAPPEN

On December 12, 1952, an experiment was being conducted at the NRX reactor, at Chalk River, Ontario. The atomic plant had been turned on at low power. One of the reactor operating crew was working in the basement of the building at an unrelated task. By mistake, he opened three or four valves he should not have; three or four (no one now recalls) of the shutoff rods lifted out of the reactor, diminishing the margin of safety.

Like atomic plants intended for electric power production, Chalk River reactor was controlled by a number of long rods inserted among the fuel tubes containing uranium, which when inserted or withdrawn, changed the rate of the nuclear chain reaction. Twelve of the rods were equipped to move very quickly; any seven of these "shutoff" rods, when inserted into the reactor, would shut it down.

When the rods withdrew, red lights began appearing on the control desk upstairs. The supervisor at the control desk telephoned to the basement to tell the operator there to stop whatever he was doing; then, leaving his assistant in charge at the control desk, the supervisor went downstairs to see what was going on.

According to the official report of the accident by W. B.

Lewis for Atomic Energy of Canada, Ltd.,[1] when the supervisor reached the basement, "He recognized the operator's mistake and was horrified at the possible consequences if the operator had continued to open these wrong valves. . . ." The supervisor then closed the valves which his subordinate had opened, assuming that the shutoff rods would then drop back into place. And, in fact, the red warning lights at the control desk went out; but the rods had only dropped a little way, enough to turn off the warning lights but not enough to reestablish the needed condition of safety. The cause of this mechanical failure has never been established—the ensuing accident obliterated its traces.

Having, as he thought, corrected the error, the supervisor telephoned upstairs to his assistant. He meant to tell the assistant to push buttons 4 and 3 on the control desk; this would have returned the whole system to normal. Instead, he said, "Push buttons 4 and 1," and immediately realizing his mistake, tried to correct it. But the assistant had already set down the phone to carry out the order. Although the reason for the order could not have been clear to him, there seemed nothing dangerous about executing it: the red warning lights had gone out.

Pushing button 1 resulted in raising four more of the shutoff rods out of the reactor; with three or four rods still withdrawn (although no one knew this yet) a total of seven or eight of the shutoff rods were out of action. The result was complete loss of the safety margin which should have been there; the level of atomic reaction occurring deep in the reactor fuel, instead of remaining steady from moment to moment, began to increase slowly.

It took a few seconds for the staff in the control room to realize that this was happening, and it was a complete surprise, but there was still no alarm. About twenty seconds after he pushed button 1, the assistant, realizing something was wrong, pushed another emergency button which should have resulted in all the shutoff rods dropping back into the reactor, shutting it down. But two of the red lights stayed on, and in fact, of the seven or eight rods which were already withdrawn, only one dropped back, and that one moved very slowly; it took about a minute and a half to fall the ten feet required.

The control room staff was now seriously concerned. The assistant hurriedly called his supervisor in the basement urging him to do something to get the rods down; meanwhile the instruments recording reactor power still showed a steady increase. As the power went on rising, it became clear that emergency measures would be needed. The precious heavy water contained in the reactor vessel would have to be dumped. The heavy water was necessary for the maintenance of the chain reaction; dumping it would stop the reactor, whatever else happened. One of the physicists in the control room was already reaching for the dump switch when the assistant supervisor gave the word.

It took some time for the heavy water to run out of the reactor; in about thirty seconds, however, instruments showed that power had dropped down to zero, and everyone breathed a sigh of relief. But the consequences of the accident had hardly begun to be felt. Down in the basement, through an open door, the supervisor could see water gushing into the room below the reactor; this was highly radioactive cooling water. Another staff member rushed to the control room to report a rumble and a spurt of water up through the top of the reactor.

At this point automatic alarms began sounding in the reactor building; radioactivity in the air had been detected by the instruments. A frantic telephone call from another building (the chemical extractions plant) revealed that high levels of radio-activity were being experienced there. Sirens were sounded, warning personnel to remain indoors. Within a few minutes the project head gave the order for the evacuation of the entire plant. Only those present in the control room donned gas masks and remained.

The whole accident inside the reactor took place in about seventy seconds, and resulted in the release, from nuclear re-action alone, of as much energy as is contained in the explosion of a half ton of TNT — although this release occurred over a period of several seconds rather than within the fraction of a second required for a violent explosion. The main immediate effect was quickly to raise the temperature of some of the ura-nium fuel past its melting point, and to cause some mild explo-sions of steam. These expelled some water from the fuel area, which in turn caused a further increase in the energy release; the water normally interfered somewhat with the atomic reac-tion, and its removal speeded up an already dangerous proc-ess.

In the rapidly increasing temperature, molten uranium and molten aluminum from the tubes which contained the fuel both mixed with the surrounding water and steam. The result was a series of chemical reactions, releasing more energy. More seri-ously, the reaction of uranium with water released free hydro-gen; air flowing into the reactor met with the hydrogen and at the high temperature caused an explosion. This explosion lifted the 4-ton gasholder dome four feet into the air and jammed it among surrounding structures.

Due to the effective functioning of emergency procedures, no one at the plant was injured during the accident, and although many were exposed to radiation, the exposures were relatively mild. The reactor core was destroyed.

The Chalk River reactor is very different in design and operation from the atomic power plants being built today. It shows clearly, however, two of the forces involved in a serious accident: the sudden release of energy by an uncontrolled atomic chain reaction, and the additional potential for explosion created by the chemical reaction of reactor materials with air and water under the suddenly high temperatures and pressures. Many of the materials used in modern reactor cores, in addition to uranium itself, react chemically with water at high temperatures.

To some extent, the Chalk River accident was caused simply by human error, and although reactor designs may change, people will always run them, and the chance of human error is always there. When it combines with mechanical failure, as at Chalk River, totally unforeseen situations may arise, and improbable results follow. In order to diminish the risk of human error, modern nuclear power plants have highly elaborate and highly complex automatic safety equipment. But these have their problems too. For complex mechanical systems sometimes behave in unforeseen and unwanted ways — as seems to have happened in the power blackout of the whole Northeast in October 1965.

All of which simply goes to say that "accidents do happen," a lesson which should not be difficult to learn in the reactor business, which has suffered a number of bad ones. Five years after Chalk River, there was another near-catastrophe, this time in England, at Windscale Pile No. 1, a reactor used for military purposes. This accident was far more serious than the one at Chalk River, and resulted not only in the total loss of the reactor, but in the release of large amounts of radioactivity into the air. Fortunately the plant was in a sparsely populated area.

Pile No. 1 is fueled with natural uranium, and is cooled, not by water as are the Chalk River and most American plants, but by air drawn through it by huge blowers and expelled, after being delayed and filtered, through high smokestacks. The heart of the reactor is a 50-foot cube of graphite, in which are inserted the long tubes of uranium fuel.

The intense radiation in a reactor induces sometimes surprising changes in the materials exposed to it. Graphite (the same material used for pencil leads) swells, and many of its physical characteristics change. The graphite is storing some of the energy of the radiation which falls on it; this energy may be released again at some unexpected time, heating the graphite and surrounding materials. The stored energy which may sometimes be released spontaneously from the graphite is named for Eugene P. Wigner, the physicist.

Since unexpected releases of heat within the complex mechanism of a reactor may cause serious damage, some means of dealing with this difficulty is needed. Quite by accident, the British discovered that heating the graphite slightly might trigger the release of the stored energy; the addition of some heat tends to trigger the release of even more heat.

In 1952, a spontaneous release of Wigner energy occurred in Windscale Pile No. 1, while the pile was shut down. Since that time regular procedures for controlling the release of Wigner energy have been carried out. On October 7, 1957 such a procedure was begun.[2]

At 1:03 A.M. the pile was shut down and the main blowers were turned off. Throughout the day a series of routine checks of the instrumentation were made, to make sure that the pile was shut down, and to test the monitoring devices within the pile.

So that the reactor operators will know what is happening within the tons of uranium which make up the core, a number of sensing devices are distributed through the fuel and the moderator. Some of these are thermocouples, which measure the temperature at different points in the uranium and graphite. The thermocouples of Pile No. 1 were carefully checked during the day of October 7 and defective ones replaced. At 7:25 P.M., all air flow through the reactor core was cut off, and the pile was started up at a low level to heat the graphite moderator. Early the next morning, the pile was again shut down.

During the morning of October 8, it seemed to the operators of the pile that the heating had not been sufficient to trigger a Wigner release, and that in fact the graphite was cooling instead of heating itself further. Examination of the records afterward showed that some of the thermocouples in the graphite did indeed show cooling, but that others registered a rising temperature.

The physicist in charge decided that a second nuclear heating was called for, and this was begun at 11:05. "The operator slipped a little bit," according to one report, "and ran the rate of reaction faster than the rules called for; however, this was not considered a very serious violation of the procedures. The rate of heating was not considered dangerous. It was merely a little bit faster than that normally carried out." [3] During the first few minutes of the heating, it was seen that the temperatures in the uranium were rising much more rapidly than was allowed under normal conditions, and therefore control rods were inserted to dampen the chain reaction and allow the uranium to cool somewhat.

Unknown to the operators of the pile, however, serious damage had already been done. Deep within the pile one or more fuel elements had seriously overheated, and their steel jackets had melted or cracked.

The second heating triggered an overall release of Wigner energy, and the temperature of the pile went on rising during Wednesday, October 9. But in the front lower portion of the pile, uranium had been exposed to the air by the failure of the fuel-element cladding, and under the high temperatures it began to burn.

The burning of these fuel elements gradually led to the failure of other nearby cartridges; the fire slowly spread, and by the following day was affecting about 150 channels.

During Wednesday, the pile instruments showed nothing wrong, except that at one point the graphite moderator was heating somewhat too rapidly. By ten o'clock the temperature recordings had risen to the point at which certain routine measures were prescribed for cooling the pile, including drawing small amounts of air through the core. Still no serious problem was detected by the reactor staff.

Before dawn on Thursday morning, instruments within the pile's smokestack indicated a rise in radioactivity, but the physicist in charge assumed that this was a normal result of the cooling air being discharged, and took no action. At noon radioactivity was detected on the roof of the weather station. The temperature of the pile continued to rise, and still more cooling air was drawn through. The smokestack meters showed a much sharper rise in radioactivity, and the pile operators realized that some of the fuel elements must have failed. There was still no hint of the fire raging within the reactor's core.

At 1:45 P.M., an attempt was made to discover where in the pile the fuel failure had occurred, but the scanning gear was

jammed and could not be moved. The radioactivity of air coming from the pile continued to increase, as did the temperature.
By this time the general manager of the pile was informed, and
he instructed the works general manager that a bad burst had
occurred. The works general manager directed that the affected fuel elements be identified and removed as soon as possible.

That afternoon, radiation workers in protective clothing entered the reactor enclosure. The radiation level of the air was
checked, and then the workers stepped onto a hoist which lifted
them to a point at the face of the pile where instruments indicated the highest temperatures. A plug in the wall of the pile
was removed, showing four uranium channels. The uranium
cartridges were seen to be at red heat.

The heat had distorted the fuel cartridges so badly that they
could not be removed. Push rods came out with molten uranium dripping from them. Surrounding cartridges were removed in an attempt to contain the fire, but the temperature
of the burning region remained very high. Although the fire
was contained in about 150 channels, the possibility existed
that further Wigner releases would occur in other regions of
the pile, adding to the total heat.

At midnight, the decision was made to use water to cool the
pile. This was a difficult decision to make, for water striking
the glowing uranium might cause an explosion. An AEC official reported later, "They will not guarantee that they could do
it a second time without an explosion." [4] The chief constable
of Cumberland was warned of the possibility of an emergency;
men in the factory were warned to stay indoors and wear face
masks. By 7:00 A.M. of October 11 it was decided that all factory personnel should be under cover. It took until nine o'clock

to institute safety precautions, and then the water was turned on. There was no explosion.

Pouring of water from hoses continued for twenty-four hours until, by Saturday afternoon, the pile was quite cold.

As a result of the accident, Windscale Pile No. 1 was a total loss. But more importantly, large amounts of radioactivity had been released from the smokestacks between October 10 and 12.

The immediate serious hazard was from iodine 131 released from the fuel of the reactor, where it was formed as a product of the breakdown of the uranium. Radioactive iodine was deposited over 200 square miles of neighboring farmland, fortunately a very sparsely inhabited area. Cows grazing in this area were removed from pasture, and the milk produced after the accident destroyed.

Drifting south and east, however, the radioactive cloud from the stacks of Windscale spread over a large area indeed. The total radioactivity released was probably about a tenth of that released during the explosion of the atomic bomb at Hiroshima, and affected a large portion of England and Northern Europe. The Danish, Netherlands, Belgian, and French governments were concerned with the increases in radioactivity in their countries as a result of this accident in northwest England.

Although Windscale Pile No. 1 was even more different from modern power reactors than the Chalk River plant, the history of its accident teaches the same lesson: there will always be an element of human failure no matter how carefully a reactor is designed; and a reactor is such a complex mechanism that very often it will behave in unexpected ways. In this case, for instance, temperature-measuring devices were distributed in the regions of highest temperature during normal operation; but during the accident, heating occurred in other areas and went undetected for more than a day.

A number of other serious reactor accidents have occurred. In 1961, another and more tragic accident occurred at a small research and training reactor in an isolated spot in Idaho. The reactor exploded, killing the three men who were tending it, and discharging some radioactivity to the surrounding area.

In 1964, T. J. Thompson of the Massachusetts Institute of Technology wrote that there had been nine serious reactivity accidents since 1949 in nonmilitary installations alone. "To date, nine [reactor fuel] cores have been destroyed or seriously damaged. . . . Three reactors have been put out of action by accidents and never revived." [5] Late in 1966 there was still another serious accident, at the Enrico Fermi plant at Lagoona Beach, Michigan; as we shall see, this accident was potentially the most serious of all.

TURNING SWORDS
INTO PLOWSHARES

ENRICO FERMI SPLIT THE ATOM IN 1934, but didn't know it. In the following four years the uranium atom was split again and again by scientists in Rome, Paris, and Berlin, but still no one recognized what was happening. Fermi wrongly believed he had created a new element, but the results were puzzling. He had bombarded uranium with the newly discovered neutron. The uranium became radioactive and seemed to take on new chemical properties, as if it had been transmuted to a new element — but the new properties were not what would have been expected.

The results were so puzzling, in fact, that the experiment was performed repeatedly by Fermi in Rome, and by other leading physicists. There was excited activity throughout the world, and no one paid any attention to an article which appeared in the German *Journal of Applied Chemistry*. The article was by a young husband-and-wife team of chemists, Ida and Walter Noddack, and they thought that Fermi was wrong. In the article they suggested: "It is conceivable that when heavy nuclei [uranium] are bombarded with neutrons those nuclei might break up into several large fragments. . . ."[1] This accurate suggestion was dismissed by Fermi and by everyone else. For it seemed obvious that the atom could not be split by the homely apparatus that Fermi had used. All the principles of physics made it clear that the nucleus of the atom could only be broken apart by vast forces, far greater than anything which scientists had been able to muster at that time.

Most physicists believed that uranium was absorbing neutrons from Fermi's device. The neutron is one of the two main components of the weight of the atom, and has no electrical charge. If the uranium in Fermi's crucible had simply absorbed neutrons, it would have been converted to a new element, and it was this that Fermi was expecting. When he did find new radioactivity and new chemical properties in the uranium exposed to his neutron gun, he assumed these were the properties of the new element. This explanation was so broadly accepted that physicists all over the world set eagerly to work to isolate the new material and explain its puzzling properties.

The properties were puzzling because there was no new element. The neutrons from Fermi's gun had not simply been absorbed by the uranium atoms; the uranium atoms had absorbed them and then split into two parts; it was these fragments that Fermi had observed. Yet physicists and chemists were repeating Fermi's experiment in an attempt to isolate and explain the surprising characteristics of the new element supposedly being created.

There was, in fact, a race to identify the new element, a race in which the winner would almost certainly receive a Nobel Prize. The leading contenders in the race were two women, Lise Meitner and Irène Joliot-Curie, who for many years had been bitter rivals. There had been sharp exchanges between them at normally sedate professional gatherings, and Fräulein Meitner had on several occasions cast doubt on the accuracy of results proceeding from Mme. Joliot-Curie's laboratory.

Women prominent in the field of physics were then as rare as they are today. Otto Hahn, a chemist who maintained a thirty-year collaboration with Lise Meitner, describes her arrival at his laboratory in the Emil Fischer Institute in Berlin, in 1907:

> In those days women were not allowed to work at the Fischer Institute. When I put the matter to Emil Fischer, he granted permission to Miss Meitner to work with me in the carpenter's shop on the ground floor of the Institute, where the radio-active measurements were carried out; he requested her, however, not to enter the study rooms on the upper floor as that would be setting a precedent.[2]

The close association between Hahn and Meitner continued until 1938 when Lise Meitner, who was Jewish, was forced to leave Berlin. The two were so much thought of as a team that when, at a professional congress, someone approached Miss Meitner with the words, "We have already met," she absent-mindedly replied, "I think you must be taking me for Professor Hahn."

Irène Joliot-Curie also had a collaborator, her husband, Pierre Joliot, who assumed his wife's distinguished name when they married. Her mother, the famous Mme. Curie, was the only person at that time to have received two Nobel Prizes, one in chemistry and one in physics, and it was believed the daughter wished to equal this achievement. She came very close indeed, having already received one Nobel Prize for the discovery of artificial radioactivity. The discovery of the first man-made element would certainly result in a second prize.

Fermi's experiment was repeated many times in both laboratories, where extensive and refined chemical techniques were used to separate the radioactive materials that resulted from neutron bombardment. Each time these separations were carried out, the result was a substance which simply could not be an element further up the atomic chain from uranium; yet despite these clear indications, no physicist could accept what was obviously happening — nuclear fission. As late as 1938, Ernest Lawrence, the inventor of the cyclotron, announced that it was as unrealistic to expect useful energy from the atom as to try to cool the ocean and use the heat extracted for practical purposes. Einstein, Planck, Bohr — all the leading physicists of the day — believed fission under ordinary circumstances to be impossible.

In the autumn of 1938, Lise Meitner slipped across the German border into the Netherlands, never to return. But Hahn remained in Berlin, carrying on his separation experiments with a colleague, Strassman. Work went on in Paris under the direction of the Joliot-Curies, and shortly after Lise Meitner's departure from Berlin, they published a paper explaining some of their previous results as errors. The results were not errors, however — they only seemed so because of the supposed impossibility of lighter elements being created from uranium. It could only have been a matter of time before the Joliot-Curies would realize the correctness of their observations, but almost immediately the paper came to the attention of Strassman, who hurried with it to Otto Hahn.

"I'm not interested in our lady friend's latest writings," Hahn replied when shown the paper. But he was finally persuaded to read it, and becoming excited, immediately set to work with Strassman. Within weeks he had confirmed the fact of nuclear fission, for which he, and not Meitner or Joliot-Curie, was to receive the Nobel Prize in 1944. He and Strassman definitely established that, mixed with their irradiated uranium, were minute quantities of barium, an element which weighs a little more than half as much as uranium, and could only have been formed by the splitting of the uranium atom. Just before Christmas of 1938, Hahn and Strassman prepared a report of their work which was published the following month. So reluctant were they to oppose the prevailing doctrines of physics, that despite the incontrovertible evidence they refused to draw a conclusion from their work.

"As chemists," they wrote, they could only conclude that barium was present in the uranium extract, "[but] as nuclear chemists, closely associated with physics, we cannot decide to take this step in contradiction to all previous experience in nuclear physics." [3]

Hahn immediately wrote to Lise Meitner, describing the results which had been made possible by the hint provided by her rival, Mme. Joliot-Curie. The implications of these experiments were immediately apparent to Meitner, spending Christmas in exile in the tiny Dutch township of Kungelv with her young nephew, O. R. Frisch. Frisch was also a physicist and a refugee, who had fled Germany to work with one of the patriarchs of physics, Niels Bohr, at his institute in Copenhagen. Avidly discussing the report from Hahn in long walks through the snow, aunt and nephew worked out the explanation of the splitting of the uranium nucleus; they quickly submitted a letter to the British journal *Nature*, which was published days after the Hahn and Strassman report. In this letter the word "fission" was first used; it was borrowed from biology where the term describes the process by which cells divide.

Events moved quickly after that. Frisch returned to Denmark, and immediately recounted the new discoveries to Niels Bohr, who was to depart the same day for the United States.

When Bohr heard Frisch's story, he slapped his forehead and cried, "How could we have overlooked that so long?" So excited did the discussion between the two physicists become that Bohr nearly missed the ship for New York, where he was to meet with Albert Einstein, another refugee of Fascism, who had settled at the Institute for Advanced Studies in Princeton.

On Monday, January 16, Bohr arrived in New York. In Princeton he told a friend, twenty-seven-year-old physicist John Wheeler, of the Hahn-Strassman experiments. Wheeler immediately arranged for a meeting to be held in Princeton the following Wednesday, at which Bohr was to tell about the splitting of the atom. Enrico Fermi, who had started it all, was not present at that meeting. He had arrived in New York just three weeks before Bohr, to take up his work at Columbia University; having just accepted a Nobel Prize in Stockholm, Fermi had decided not to return to Fascist Italy, and had brought his family to America. A young colleague, Willis Lamb, then a twenty-five-year-old physics instructor at Columbia, brought him the news of the revelations Bohr was making in Princeton, the explanation of the five-year-long mystery of Fermi's own experiments.

Fermi immediately designed an experiment to confirm the new results, but he did not wait for the confirmation. He had a date to meet with Bohr the next morning in Washington, at a conference on theoretical physics. Fermi apparently had no doubt that fission had indeed taken place; his meeting with Bohr in Washington on the morning of Thursday, January 26, 1939, was the first step on the road which would lead him to Alamogordo and the nation to Hiroshima, and a nuclear arms race.

That Thursday morning Fermi and Bohr sat at the back of a

classroom in George Washington University, talking excitedly, oblivious to the meeting going on around them. They knew that discoveries of vast importance to physics had been made, but they had not yet realized the importance of nuclear fission to a world at war. For the practical importance of atomic energy depended on two factors, one of which would be resolved in weeks; the other would not be settled for years.

The first factor was the possibility of a chain reaction. A uranium nucleus, struck with a neutron, splits. The neutron has less than one electron volt of energy; fragments of the split atom carry 200 million electron volts. This is clearly an unprecedented multiplication of force. But an atom is, after all, very small. The energy released by the fission of a single uranium atom can only be detected by sensitive instruments.

But what if, when the uranium nucleus splits, it produces two new neutrons? Each of these would then split two more atoms, which would produce four neutrons to split four atoms, which would produce eight neutrons, and so on. If, as Fermi and Bohr had already realized, fission produced neutrons, a chain reaction would be possible, and a single neutron would act like a match to touch off an atomic fire of unprecedented power. On March 3, 1939, the Hungarian physicist Leo Szilard performed an experiment at Columbia University which confirmed Fermi's prediction that neutrons would be produced by fission: the practical release of atomic energy was possible.

But there was still another difficulty to overcome, and in the early days of 1939 it seemed to the physicists nearly insurmountable. It became clear in those early discussions that only a tiny fraction of natural uranium could be fissioned. More than 99 percent of uranium as it is found in nature is in the form of U-238, the isotope which has 238 protons and neutrons in its nucleus. About seven-tenths of one percent of the mineral is U-235, an isotope with three fewer neutrons. Only this seven-tenths of one percent could be split by neutrons. U-238 would not fission — and, furthermore, it would absorb neutrons without being split, and would thus interfere with a chain reaction occurring in the U-235.

There would be no difficulty if there were an easy way of separating the two isotopes of uranium, but this was, and is, an enormously difficult job. The two isotopes of uranium do not differ in any way except for the tiny difference — three parts in 238 — in their atomic weights. The chemical properties of the two forms are identical, and they cannot be separated by ordinary chemical means. Methods of separating isotopes in minute quantities for laboratory work were known, but doing so on a commercial scale seemed to the physicists very difficult. But should it be possible, the implications were clear.

A chain reaction, if it were possible at all, would occur very quickly, releasing a great deal of energy in a very short period of time. And this is simply a definition of an explosion. An atomic bomb was possible — and this would be as obvious to German physicists as to the newly arrived Americans. It was obvious also to a *New York Times* science reporter named William Laurence. On February 24, Fermi and Bohr were again at a meeting together, this time the annual meeting of the American Physical Society at Columbia University. Laurence was covering the meeting for the *Times,* and when he heard Fermi suggest that a chain reaction was possible, he immediately saw the implications.

"Could not a small quantity of uranium 235, say just one kilogram, be used as a bomb equal to thousands of tons of TNT?" Laurence asked Fermi and Bohr after the meeting.

In his book, *Men and Atoms*,[4] Laurence says that Fermi replied, "We must not jump to hasty conclusions," in an attempt to discourage curiosity, for plans were already being discussed to alert the United States Government to possibilities in nuclear fission. Unaware of the scientists' efforts along these lines, and believing that the Germans might be stealing a march, Laurence began accumulating material for a newspaper article which he hoped would focus American attention on the atom. The painstaking accumulation of the evidence that German scientists were indeed working on fission took a full year. On May 5, 1940, the story appeared on the front page of the *Times*:

VAST POWER SOURCE
IN ATOMIC ENERGY
OPENED BY SCIENCE

*Relative of Uranium Found to
Yield Force 5 Million Times
as Potent as Coal*

Germany Is Seeking It

The article described accurately the enormous power latent in uranium for commercial application and for destruction. To Laurence's surprise, there was no reaction from the U.S. Government at all. Persuaded of the importance of his message, Laurence tried again, this time by submitting a similar article to the *Saturday Evening Post*, which was accepted only when it had been certified as accurate by an imposing array of the country's most prominent physicists. The article finally appeared in September of 1940 — and again, there was no reaction from Washington. The accuracy of Laurence's statements was attested to somewhat later by the Government, however. As Laurence writes,

> Early in the Spring of 1945, after I had been invited to join the inner circle of the atomic-bomb project, I learned, to my amazement, that the [*Saturday Evening Post*] article had been classified as secret and that I would not be permitted to carry it around with me. A copy in my briefcase was stamped "Secret" and solemnly locked in a large safe.[5]

Although Laurence did not know it, similar efforts to bring the atom to official attention were being made by scientists, and meeting with as little success. Fermi approached the Navy Department and was rebuffed. Finally, in 1941, on the eve of the Japanese attack on Pearl Harbor, atomic energy was brought to President Roosevelt's attention through a letter signed by Albert Einstein. By the following year the Manhattan Engineer District, the code name for the all-out effort to produce an atomic bomb, had come into being.

Far more attention was given in those early days of atomic energy to its commercial applications than is now realized, when nuclear weapons have come to overshadow so much of our thought. The French government, for instance, seemed to have been primarily interested in postwar commercial applications of atomic energy. In 1939, Joliot-Curie approached the French Minister of Munitions, who showed great interest in atomic energy. Patents were quickly filed in Swiss patent offices. German scientists apparently also devoted much effort, during the war, to industrial applications of fission. In this country too the difficulties of producing a nuclear weapon seemed very great, if not insurmountable; without the threat of a German atom bomb, we would not have tried to build ours before the end of the war. Industrial applications seemed to hold more promise. As late as 1941, there was still no major effort devoted to weapons development in this country, but in that year Arthur Holly Compton, famous for his work on X-rays, approached General Electric regarding potential industrial atomic development. He reports that GE was quite interested.[6] But by December of that year, the Federal Government preempted the nuclear field, and we entered the war ourselves.

In March of 1939, when Szilard and others confirmed the fact that neutrons were produced each time a uranium nucleus fissioned, it was clear that an atomic bomb was possible in theory. Yet the construction of such a bomb seemed terribly difficult because of the necessity for separating fissionable uranium 235 from the overwhelming amounts of uranium 238, which seemed a near impossible task. And in fact, if this were the only way of making an atom bomb, the attempt might never have been made.

To use atomic energy for industrial purposes, such as the production of electricity, it would not be necessary to separate the two isotopes of uranium, and might not even be desirable to do so. When the nucleus of the U-235 atom splits, two or three neutrons on the average are expelled at enormous speeds. In a block of natural uranium, there are 139 atoms of U-238 for each atom of U-235. It is therefore most likely that these speeding neutrons, if they do not escape entirely, will strike not another U-235 atom, but an unfissionable U-238. They will be absorbed, and the chain reaction will end before it has begun.

But U-235 has a peculiar characteristic which will be best understood by golfers: they know that when putting, if they hit the ball too hard, it will go right over the hole without dropping in. Only a slowly moving ball will be "captured." So with

U-235 — a neutron moving slowly has a greater chance of being captured by a U-235 atom and splitting it than a fast neutron like those produced by fission. U-238, on the other hand,
usually absorbs only fast neutrons. Slow neutrons therefore
usually bounce harmlessly off U-238 until they hit a U-235 atom.

It is possible to sustain a chain reaction in natural uranium
without separating the U-235 and U-238, by slowing the neutrons produced by fission. Slowing down neutrons is not as
difficult as it sounds. Fermi had done it in those historic experiments of 1934, simply by passing the neutrons through water
or graphite before they hit his uranium "target." The water
slowed the neutrons because each neutron collided with many
water molecules before it could escape.

Fermi applied this principle in the first major construction of
the Manhattan Project, in 1942. He and his colleagues worked
in an abandoned squash court under Stagg Field at the University of Chicago. A brass plaque for years hung modestly on a
wire fence at the site, commemorating the achievement of the
group:

ON DECEMBER 2, 1942
MAN ACHIEVED HERE
THE FIRST SELF-SUSTAINING CHAIN REACTION
AND THEREBY INITIATED THE
CONTROLLED RELEASE OF NUCLEAR ENERGY

What Fermi and his group had done was to build the world's
first nuclear reactor, the distant ancestor of the huge nuclear
power plants now rising outside the country's major cities. It
was a surprisingly simple device: a pile of graphite blocks in
which blocks of uranium metal and uranium oxide were placed
in alternate layers of the graphite. When an atom of U-235 in

one of the blocks of uranium fissioned, usually two or three neutrons would streak away at enormous speed and go crashing into the surrounding graphite where, after repeated collisions, they would be slowed but not absorbed. Eventually the neutrons would pass through another of the blocks of uranium; already moving too slowly to be easily absorbed by U-238, the neutrons would bounce off these atoms until finally they would encounter an atom of U-235, split it and start the process all over again.

Some of the neutrons, of course, would escape from the pile without ever encountering a U-235 atom. Others would be absorbed by impurities in the uranium and graphite. But if one neutron found its way back to a U-235 atom for each atom which split, the chain reaction would be "self-sustaining": it would go on at a steady, constant rate. If two of the neutrons produced in each fission went on to split other U-235 atoms, the reaction would grow very quickly to the point of an explosion.

In order to keep the reaction under control, long rods of cadmium were inserted into the pile; these were its only moving parts. Cadmium is a material which absorbs neutrons; as long as the "control rods" were fully inserted, they would absorb too many of the neutrons for a chain reaction to occur. On December 2, 1942, these rods were slowly withdrawn. The number of neutrons free in the pile slowly increased until there were slightly more neutrons colliding with U-235 atoms and splitting them than there were the moment before. The number of fissions began to increase geometrically, and a recording pen that Fermi and his fellow scientists watched began tracing a slow curve that turned upward at an ever increasing rate. The pile was "critical." Fermi signaled to the young physicist George Weil to reinsert the cadmium control rod; Eugene Wigner produced a bottle of Chianti and toasts were drunk from paper cups. The atomic age had begun.

The first reactor, or "pile" as it was then called, was not built with industrial applications in mind. It was a test of a method of producing plutonium for atomic weapons, but it was also the forerunner of modern nuclear electric power stations.

Ordinary power plants make electricity from the heat of burning coal, oil or gas, or from the power of falling water. Atomic power plants make electricity from the heat of splitting atoms.

Nuclear power plants are now usually called reactors, simply because they are little more, at bottom, than containers in which atomic reactions go on. The typical nuclear power reactor holds many tons of uranium in a cylindrical steel container. When enough uranium sufficiently rich in U-235 is assembled in one place and is interspersed with water or similar material to slow or "moderate" neutrons, it undergoes atomic reaction and becomes very hot. The problem in an ordinary power plant is to keep the fire going; in an atomic power plant the problem is to keep it from getting out of hand. The steel vessel filled with uranium would simply go on getting hotter and hotter until it exploded, unless control devices were inserted.

The reactor at its simplest is therefore a steel vessel containing uranium: the uranium fuel is ordinarily packed into long narrow tubes which are collected in bundles called "fuel assemblies." Long control rods among the fuel tubes regulate the rate of reaction — and hence the heat produced. Water is pumped into the vessel and comes in contact with the hot fuel tubes. Steam is produced and drawn off, and from there an atomic power plant is just like any other. The steam turns the blades of turbines, which drive generators which make electricity.

This seems a simple and cheap way to make electric power, for uranium releases huge amounts of energy when its atoms split. One   pound of uranium 235 contains the energy of millions of pounds of coal. In the late 1940's, when atomic power plants were first being discussed publicly, highly respected individuals predicted that the atom would make electricity too cheap to meter. And although this has not turned out to be quite the case, atomic power plants are becoming cheaper and are appearing on the outskirts of our largest cities — New York, Boston, Chicago, Los Angeles, Detroit, and San Francisco. By the early 1970's there will be more than a hundred of these plants operating, most of them enormous, capable of producing a million kilowatts of power, more than enough power for a city of a million inhabitants. By the end of the century, half of all America's electricity is expected to come from the atom.

And yet, despite the optimistic prophecies of the 1940's, the present economic success of nuclear power plants has been a surprise to nearly everyone. During its first eight years of operation, the Atomic Energy Commission, civilian successor to the wartime Manhattan Project, was preoccupied with the problems of developing and building nuclear weapons. It was not until the mid-1950's that pressure from Congress and industry forced an expanded program of civilian atomic power plant development. As late as 1961, fully two-thirds of the AEC's reactor budget was devoted to military applications.

The principal military applications of reactors were for use in nuclear submarines and for the production of plutonium.

The second application prompted construction of the world's first reactor at the University of Chicago during the Second World War. In the early days of the Manhattan Project, two approaches were taken toward atomic weapons construction. The first was the attempt to isolate essentially pure uranium 235 from the nonfissionable and hence nonexplosive, but far more abundant, uranium 238 with which it is mixed in nature. This was considered an extremely difficult and uncertain task, and a second back-up method was also tried.

Fermi and his co-workers had shown that when natural uranium, a mixture of U-235 and U-238, was combined with graphite, the U-235 could sustain a chain reaction despite the presence of large quantities of U-238, which acted like an impurity, absorbing neutrons and thus poisoning the chain reaction. It had long been known, however, that when U-238 absorbed neutrons it was converted to a new element. This new element, plutonium, had first been produced in literally microscopic quantities by a group headed by Dr. Glenn Seaborg, at Berkeley, California, by bombarding uranium 238 with neutrons produced in a cyclotron. Seaborg therefore reached the goal (and eventually the Nobel Prize) which had been sought so long, but by the wrong paths, by Lise Meitner and Irène Joliot-Curie. But his results were far more important than those two distinguished ladies could have guessed. As had been predicted by L. A. Turner of Princeton, plutonium was like uranium 235 — it could sustain a chain reaction and therefore could be used to construct an atom bomb.

Only infinitesimal quantities of plutonium could be produced by Seaborg's method; but Fermi's atomic pile represented a means of making far more. A pile, or reactor, could be built as large as one liked, which meant that enormous numbers of neutrons could be produced in a controlled chain reaction, and these could transform the uranium 238 which was a constituent of the reactor into plutonium. The plutonium could then be extracted by conventional chemical processes.

This method was proved a success during the war. Enormous plutonium production reactors were built near Richland, Washington, on the Columbia River. At the peak of wartime construction, 45,000 workers were engaged at the reactor site. By 1945, enough plutonium had been produced to build the bomb (called "fat man" by its builders) which destroyed the city of Nagasaki. The devastation of Hiroshima, however, was accomplished with a bomb made of uranium 235 which had been separated from the more common but less explosive form of the element by a process called gaseous diffusion.

Although U-235 has proved to be the cheaper of the two bomb materials, this country has constructed fourteen plutonium production reactors. Nine of these were built at the wartime site of Hanford, near Richland, Washington; five were built on the Savannah River in South Carolina. These supplement the gaseous diffusion plants for separation of U-235 which produce most of our atomic weapons.

Although the size and characteristics of the plutonium production reactors are classified information, they are clearly very big. Published estimates indicate that on the average each plant produces well over one million kilowatts of heat energy. This is the heat produced in the chain reaction, and for most of the reactors it is simply a dangerous nuisance. If this waste heat were to be harnessed, however, it could be used to produce large blocks of electric power.

The possibility of using plutonium production reactors for a second purpose, electric power generation, and thus making them far more economical, was obvious from the outset, but in fact it was not realized except in one case, the New Production Reactor completed in 1965. Electric power from this plutonium production reactor is generated and distributed by the Washington Public Power Supply System.

The pressures of stockpiling Cold War weapons prevented the AEC from paying much attention to electric power production until fairly recently, but it was always clear that this aspect of reactors would not be indefinitely ignored. During the 1950's there was considerable uneasiness among the private, or investor-owned, utilities over the Federal Government's growing investment in reactors which could be used for power production. It was probably the concern among the private utilities over this potential new source of public power that accounted for their eagerness, in the 1950's, to participate in the atomic energy program.

Reactors for plutonium production therefore provided the basic principles and the initial economic impetus toward nuclear power plants. With major reactor development efforts in other military applications, it is not surprising that the form civilian plants eventually took was also heavily influenced by military projects.

The most obvious application for atomic power plants is in military submarines. Unlike conventional oil-burning engines which need air for combustion, reactors require no air for their operation. Reactors are compact. They do not need to be refueled except at long intervals. In short, they are ideal for a submarine which must stay under water for long periods of time.

Several reactor designs were experimented with for submarine propulsion, but the final choice was a type called the "pressurized water" reactor, built by the Westinghouse Electric Corporation. In this type, cooling water is circulated through the reactor under pressure, so that it does not boil. After leaving the reactor core, this water passes through pipes in a boiler, where steam is produced, before being returned to cool the reactor again.

Westinghouse has now become one of the two manufacturers which supply the majority of reactors for civilian power production. All Westinghouse plants, including the country's first reactor to produce power for commercial use, have been developed from the power plants which drive nuclear submarines and surface ships. This is not to imply that Westinghouse has taken undue advantage of its position as a defense contractor. The basic design of the pressurized water reactor, like the designs of other types, is in the public domain and freely available from the AEC.

Westinghouse is also one of the principal suppliers of conventional electric generating equipment; its main rival is the General Electric Company. With a potential market for reactors provided by private utilities trying to forestall federal atomic power generation, and with its chief competitor engaged in reactor development, General Electric quickly came up with a rival model, the boiling water reactor. This was a type first developed for research purposes at the Atomic Energy Commission's Argonne Laboratory. It differed from the pressurized water reactor in that there was no separate boiler — the steam was generated right in the reactor core and drawn off to the turbines.

GE and Westinghouse dominated the reactor field from the outset, and continue to do so. Of the reactors ordered through

1967, the two firms divided 80 percent about equally between them. The remainder were supplied by Combustion Engineering and Babcock and Wilcox, two major suppliers of conventional boilers.

While atomic energy was under military control, and then for eight years more under the Atomic Energy Act of 1946, only the Government could build or own reactors. A new Atomic Energy Act passed in 1954 opened the door to private ownership. In 1955, the Atomic Energy Commission announced the Cooperative Power Reactor Demonstration Program, through which utilities could obtain heavy federal assistance in building nuclear plants. Shortly thereafter, two utilities announced plans to build reactors with their own funds, although receiving substantial indirect subsidies from the Government in the form of reduced fuel costs, design assistance, waste disposal services, and others. The Consolidated Edison Company, which supplies New York City, announced plans to build a Westinghouse reactor on the Hudson River; Commonwealth Edison announced that it would build a General Electric reactor near Chicago. Ten other utilities, both investor-owned and publicly owned, announced plans for small plants under the cooperative demonstration program, and received substantial direct and indirect assistance.

The dozen atomic power plants which were to be built by utilities alone or in cooperation with the AEC ran into trouble from the outset. The Fermi plant at Lagoona Beach, Michigan, near Detroit, never succeeded in producing substantial amounts of electric power. The plant at Hallam, Nebraska, after a long history of difficulties, was finally shut down, and at this writing is being dismantled, while a coal-burning plant rises to replace it. All of the other plants experienced technical difficulties, soaring costs, and long delays. A mood of gloom settled over the nuclear industry.

By 1963, the prospects for civilian atomic power looked bleak. Manufacturing firms which had entered the nuclear field during its first flowering, five years before, were announcing plans to withdraw. Utilities seemed to have lost interest in reactors, and violent legal battles were being fought with citizens' groups contesting the safety of those reactors which were being built. A highly respected study by the economist Philip Mullenbach, for the Twentieth Century Fund, summed up the prevailing attitude:

> . . . the fact is that private utilities, eight years after the passage of the 1954 [atomic energy] act, had constructed only two full-scale plants without heavy government assistance, and these two were among the very first announced. The evidence raises the question whether the private utilities are prepared even at this late date to make the large investments called for by full-scale nuclear power.[7]

Yet at almost the same time these words were published, the New Jersey Central Power and Light Company announced that it had reached an agreement with General Electric to purchase a reactor capable of generating more than 500,000 kilowatts, twice the size of any previously built. The utility planned to ask for no federal assistance — but what was more surprising, its calculations showed that the nuclear plant would produce power more cheaply than a coal plant at the same site. This was the first plant to be chosen on strictly economic grounds: for the first time, nuclear power could compete with coal.

It may be that General Electric had stolen a march by providing guaranteed prices and performance for the New Jersey plant to be built at Oyster Creek that meant no profit, and perhaps a loss, to the manufacturer. Although the plant is not yet in operation, it has already suffered a number of technical setbacks which have put it far behind schedule, and which will put its cost to both manufacturer and utility beyond that which had been announced.

Nevertheless, the Oyster Creek announcement was heralded as the long-awaited breakthrough in reactor economics. By 1965, when it seemed clear that both General Electric and Westinghouse were willing to sell reactors on similar terms for other locations, a flood of orders began pouring in which has not yet abated. By April of 1968, about 100 reactors were operating, under construction, or being ordered. During 1966 and 1967, more than half the generating capacity of new plants ordered in the United States was nuclear, and this pace has continued into 1968.

The plants being ordered now are twice the size of Oyster Creek, and it is hoped by the manufacturers and the utilities that the economies of size will, in fact, make those new plants cheaper than coal plants in almost all parts of the country. Whether or not the economic realities will confirm these predictions is yet to be seen. The sudden and largely unexpected rush to reactors has created some far more serious problems.

Because of military, political, and economic pressures, it has never been possible to question seriously the present need for atomic power, nor to choose among the various routes to that goal which are available. With few exceptions, there has been no public discussion whatever of the benefits and risks of our present nuclear power program. One of those exceptions, and the most notable is, as might be expected, in California.

EARTHQUAKES AND ACCIDENTS

CALIFORNIA ROUTE 1 IS A TWO-LANE HIGHWAY; going north
from San Francisco it edges the Pacific Coast, in a series of
roller-coaster curves on the hills which rise from the sea there.
For a while it flattens out as it skirts inland of Tomales Bay.
Then the open sea is in view again for a while and the hills
return. About fifty miles north of San Francisco, the highway
passes the tiny town of Bodega Bay. The Bay is formed by a
rocky peninsula, Bodega Head, which arches in a curve west
and south and ends in a granite hammerhead. This isolated
and beautiful spot was to be the site of one of the country's
most controversial peacetime atomic ventures.

A left turn from Route 1 will take you into the small fishing
village of Bodega Bay. The Bay is the first harbor of refuge
north of San Francisco, and it is crowded with fishing boats.
There is a new four-lane road around the shore of the harbor.
It runs past a cluster of piers and houses on the east shore and
sweeps on to the west shore, the inner side of the peninsula.
Here the houses quickly disappear; the road runs on over what
was once a series of rocky tidal pools rich in marine life. A
stranger wonders what optimistic town plan produced this
four-lane road running down deserted Bodega Head.

The road runs past a long galvanized-wire fence and finally

ends in a parking area. But there is nothing here, and seemingly nothing within the fence. Very near the end of the peninsula, in an indentation in the granite hill on the harbor side, is a large circular hole, now filled with water, and a heap of gravel long abandoned. There are no placards or other signs to mark this as the location of what was to have been the Pacific Gas and Electric Company's Bodega Bay Atomic Park. After more than six years of planning and battle the Pacific Gas and Electric Company on October 30, 1964, announced that it had abandoned plans for a nuclear-powered electric generating plant at Bodega Bay. On the following day the San Francisco *Chronicle* reported:

> The site, only 1000 feet west of the San Andreas fault, was dropped as the location for a 325,000-kilowatt nuclear plant because of fears that dangerous radiation would be released in case of a severe earthquake.

In making his brief announcement, Robert H. Gerdes, then president of P. G. & E., stated, according to the *Chronicle*, "We would be the last to desire to build a plant with any substantial doubt existing as to public safety." [1]

The statement must have been a difficult one for Gerdes to make, for the investment in the Bodega Bay Atomic Park had already reached $4 million in planning and construction costs alone. The additional investment of the private utility's talent, time, and money in the six-year battle against public opposition to the nuclear reactor at Bodega will probably never be known.

Early in 1958, Pacific Gas and Electric began bargaining for land on Bodega Head. To the country's largest privately owned utility, with assets in the billions, this must have seemed a minor element of routine. Several months before, P. G. & E. officers had met privately and in secret with the Board of Supervisors of Sonoma County. Supervisor E. J. ("Nin") Guidotti later recalled, "We were all aware of the possibility that [the plant] would be nuclear."[2] But no public announcement was made.

P. G. & E. had announced that it planned to add some nuclear plants to its generating capacity, but it did not say whether the Bodega site would house one of the new plants. At this time there was only one nuclear plant in the country producing commercial electric power, the Shippingport atomic plant in Pennsylvania. P. G. & E. was therefore perhaps a little hesitant about public reaction to a neighboring atomic power plant; whatever its reasons, the announcement that the Bodega plant was to be nuclear did not come until nearly three years after the utility began acquiring land. The secrecy with which these early steps were taken did not avoid local opposition to the plant, however. Opposition began almost at the outset, and stemmed at first from Rose Gaffney, who owned a little more than four hundred acres of Bodega Head.

Bodega was then a very beautiful and largely undisturbed place, with a long if quiet history. A Russian sealing station had been there. The Mexicans and the Americans followed in slow succession; there is no drama in Bodega's history. It was a beautiful peaceful spot, and Rose Gaffney's title to her land was originally granted in Mexico City, not Washington, D.C. It is dry, rocky ground. In recent years Mrs. Gaffney had derived a small income from it by renting it for pasturage; a small dairy herd grazed the hills which were brown in summer, green in winter.

The California State Department of Recreation had long wanted Bodega Head as a park; the University of California was considering setting up a marine biology laboratory. But for the time being, control of the area was vested in the County Board of Supervisors, and they had probably already agreed, in private, to P. G. & E.'s plans for the area. When in 1958 Rose Gaffney refused to sell her land to the utility, P. G. & E. quietly went to court and, still with no public announcement, initiated condemnation proceedings. A utility has the right of eminent domain — Mrs. Gaffney could be forced to sell her land.

The long battle which Mrs. Gaffney fought to keep from meeting P. G. & E.'s demands disrupted what might have been a smooth and orderly progress to a nuclear plant. Coupled with opposition in the town of Bodega Head and Sonoma County over a variety of issues, ranging from different plans for the development of the harbor area to a general concern over preserving the natural beauty of Bodega Head, Mrs. Gaffney's vociferous reluctance delayed and publicized P. G. & E.'s plans to the point that organized public opposition on a large scale became possible. A remarkably effective organization, the Northern California Association to Preserve Bodega Head and Harbor, whose membership eventually numbered in the thousands, came into existence, and was headed by a young Sierra Club staff member named David Pesonen.

Opposition to the Bodega plant quickly centered on conservation issues; Bodega Head had unique scientific and recreational values which would be destroyed by the plant. It was not until the summer of 1961 that P. G. & E. finally announced what had already been widely assumed in the press — the power plant at Bodega was to use atomic fuel. With this announcement the already organized opposition focused on a new issue: safety. For the site of the plant was only 1000 feet from the San Andreas fault, the most active source of earthquakes in the country, and the cause of the 1906 earthquake which devastated San Francisco.

In 1965, Dr. Edward Teller, often called the "father of the H-Bomb," and not otherwise noted for his caution in advocating the military development of atomic energy, wrote in 1965: "In principle, nuclear reactors are dangerous. . . . By being careful, and also by good luck, we have so far avoided all serious nuclear accidents. . . . In my mind, nuclear reactors do not belong on the surface of the earth. Nuclear reactors belong underground." [3] It is easy to see the cause of Dr. Teller's trepidation. As we shall see, the results of a serious accident involving a reactor could be disastrous; if anything could cause such an accident, an earthquake might.

A reactor like the one planned for Bodega is a complex and temperamental device, under the best of circumstances. It would seem unreasonable to expect such a device to go on functioning safely during an earthquake; yet this is precisely what the designers of the P. G. & E. plant intended. For it was clear that sometime during the lifetime of the reactor there might be another severe earthquake at the San Andreas fault. Light warning tremors are a commonplace in the area; severe earthquakes have occurred several times, the worst having been in 1906. The earthquake which more recently devastated the Alaskan coast was due to the same system of faults.

The world's worst earthquake zones lie in a circle around the Pacific Ocean. The earthquakes which periodically rack the western coast of the United States, and the devastating earthquake which struck Alaska on Good Friday of 1964, all lie within this circum-Pacific ring of earthquakes and volcanoes.

Earthquakes are not very well understood, nor are their causes certain. They are reminders that the crust of the earth which seems so solid and immutable is in slow but constant change, and that the seemingly fixed continents are slowly rearing upward or sinking back into the sea. The slow massive movements of the earth's crust sometimes become visible to us, when growing stresses in the crust cause earthquakes.

Past geological stresses have left long cracks or faults in many parts of the world. The earthquake ring around the Pacific is a network of such faults, some of which may run for hundreds of miles. When the slow shifting in the earth's crust builds up stress in the rock, it may give suddenly, often along the line of such a fault. This sudden readjustment is an earthquake; close to the fault the earth on both sides snaps away with great force in a whiplash motion. This sudden snapping release is accompanied by the enormous vibration of readjustment, as one side of the fault grinds against the other. During the 1906 earthquake in San Francisco, the earth shifted along the fault 20 feet in some places; the west side of the fault was two or three feet higher than the east side after the earthquake.

The San Francisco earthquake was due to shifting on the San Andreas fault, the most active earthquake zone in the country, along the shoreline of California. At Bodega it actually runs through the Bay. The proposed site of the atomic power plant which Pacific Gas and Electric planned to build at Bodega was about 1000 feet from the edge of the San Andreas fault zone, despite a clear regulation of the Atomic Energy Commission that "no facility should be located closer than one fourth mile from the surface location of a known

active earthquake fault." This means that the Bodega plant
was to have been 320 feet closer than it should have been.

Pacific Gas and Electric maintained that the reactor could
be built to ride out any major earthquake which might occur
during the plant's lifetime. The Atomic Energy Commission's
prestigious Advisory Committee on Reactor Safeguards gave
preliminary agreement to the plan, but, late in 1964, the AEC's
own staff expressed some doubts, and P. G. & E. withdrew their
application. Yet for three years they had maintained the safety
of the atomic plant in the face of growing opposition and technical disagreement.

Bodega Head is an ancient granite formation, and at first
sight would seem to provide the solid rock anchorage which
is ideal for structures which hope to ride out the shock of a
nearby earthquake. Even though the proposed site was close to
the San Andreas fault, it was thought to be outside the "zone
of fling" — the area bordering the fault where the earth snaps
away during an earthquake. The Bodega site would only suffer
the shocks, transmitted through the ground, of the earthquake
readjustment, but there would be no shifting on Bodega Head
itself. In principle it seemed possible to build a building which
would ride out the shock waves, although what effect such
drastic shocks would have on the delicate mechanism of a
reactor was hard to foretell. P. G. & E. maintained in its original
application that no matter what damage was suffered by the
reactor core itself during an earthquake, the containment structure to be provided would assure that there would be no release of radioactivity to the outside air to pose a hazard to
nearby residents.

This approach is typical of all builders of modern power
reactors. It is generally recognized that our understanding of

reactors is not good enough for us to rule out absolutely the possibility of a drastic mishap in the reactor itself, and correspondingly each reactor is equipped with a number of devices designed to reduce the consequences of such an accident, should it happen. In many reactors the ultimate line of defense is the containment sphere, a steel or concrete dome designed hopefully to contain all or most of the radiation which would be released in a major reactor accident.

The Bodega reactor was to have a different sort of containment, a "pressure suppression" system, which had only been tried once before at the far-smaller installation at Humboldt Bay, California. This would provide a huge doughnut-ring suppression pool, half filled with water, around the reactor. Any build-up of pressure in the reactor, as in an accident, would vent harmlessly into the pool; radioactive wastes would be contained in the pool and in a steel drywell which surrounded the reactor core.

Opposition to the reactor had originally been in terms of conserving the unique natural qualities of Bodega Head. When serious safety problems about the Bodega site began to appear, the Northern California Association to Preserve Bodega Head and Harbor, led by David Pesonen, was able to marshal an impressive body of expert testimony and independent information. An early problem to appear was that the site of the reactor, supposed to be solid rock, was in fact the sloping side of an ancient canyon which had long ago filled with sediment. Preliminary borings on the site showed almost 60 feet of silt, clay, and sand. Dr. Pierre Saint-Amand, a professional seismologist from the Naval Ordnance Testing Station, China Lake, California, a man very well known in this field, and later a member of the team sent by the governor of California to

survey the effects of the Alaskan earthquake and to make recommendations to prevent similar damage to structures in
California, was retained by Pesonen's group to give an independent evaluation of the reactor site. Saint-Amand's report
read in part:

> It is generally thought that it is better to build upon solid rock
> than upon alluvium. This is certainly true at a distance from the
> causative fault. However, at near fault distances, where fling is
> important, rock may be as bad or worse. Clearly the worst pos-
> sible situation is to build upon a combination of the two. At the
> Bodega Head site the rock is severely crushed, broken and
> mylonitized. It could scarcely be classed as good foundation
> material. It will transmit well high-frequency vibrations, and
> then plastically deform in response to regional readjustment of
> strain; it will probably also undergo mass movement due to its
> own weight during the long-period oscillations. In addition,
> the alluvium, a loosely aggregated clay-rich soil, will certainly
> yield at a different rate than the rock, subjecting the installation
> to widely varying dynamic loads and permitting the several parts
> of the installation to settle different amounts, probably resulting
> in serious damage from changes in level and position to intercon-
> necting structures, to the cooling system, and to the reactor itself.
> A worse foundation situation would be difficult to envision.[4]

This report was made during 1963; shortly after it was issued,
a team from the United States Geological Survey visited the
site. By this time preliminary construction had begun, including the first excavation of the shaft in which the reactor itself would be housed. USGS investigators Schlocker and Bonilla
first visited the site in the summer of 1963, and then were called
back to it in October. A fault running through the reactor
shaft itself had been discovered.

The two geologists remained at the site while construction progressed. When the shaft was 142 feet in diameter and 73 feet below sea level, Schlocker and Bonilla examined the shaft and reported, in January 1964, that running through the reactor site was,

> an important zone of weakness that could undergo differential movement if stressed to a degree comparable to the stress applied to granitic rocks on [nearby] Point Reyes peninsula during the 1906 earthquake.[5]

As David Pesonen noted later in a pamphlet, "One of the most important findings of this report . . . was that during the 1906 earthquake there had been significant faulting of the rock on Point Reyes, *outside* the commonly accepted San Andreas Zone." [6] What had happened at nearby and geologically similar Point Reyes could easily happen at the reactor site on Bodega Head.

This discovery put a very different light on the problem of the safety of the site. P. G. & E.'s own former consultant, geologist Dr. William Quaide, stated to a San Francisco *Chronicle* reporter: "There is a chance that the fault could break beneath the plant's site in case of an earthquake. I think the probability is low. . . . But it is necessary to face the moral issue: 'If there is even a slight chance of danger, should we go ahead and build the plant?' " [7]

P. G. & E. insisted on the low probability of movement along the fault through the reactor site, and in its own report on the situation noted that there was no evidence of movement along the fault "during the last 40,000 years." [8]

The otherwise unsuitable characteristics of the site became

submerged in the debate over whether there would actually be slippage along the fault running through the reactor site. Dr. George Housner, P. G. & E.'s consultant on design and a widely respected professor of structural engineering at the California Institute of Technology, reported to the Company in 1961:

> Since it is quite impossible to design a power plant to survive without damage the large permanent ground surface displacements that might occur if earthquake fault slippage occurred on the site, this possibility must be given special consideration.[9]

The Atomic Energy Commission eventually insisted that this serious possibility must be taken into account, and asked P. G. & E. to amend its application for a construction permit. The company responded by submitting Amendment 7 to its Hazards Analysis, offering a novel design to "accommodate movement along [the fault on the site], even though the possibility of such movement occurring is not considered to be credible." The novel design, never before used in a civilian structure, was apparently based on the design of underground siloes which protect this country's intercontinental ballistic missiles against nuclear attack.

The tenacity with which Pacific Gas and Electric clung to the Bodega site despite the mounting evidence of its unsuitability is quite puzzling. Some support, it was true, was given by the AEC's Advisory Committee on Reactor Safeguards which approved the site. It was only in the face of almost certain disapproval by the Atomic Energy Commission itself that the application for the reactor was withdrawn. Although $4 million had been invested in the Bodega site, the multibillion dol-

lar utility would certainly have weathered the loss easily.
What may have been more important was the utility's much
greater commitment to nuclear power in general. Plans called
for an increasing reliance of the company on nuclear plants
in California, where air pollution problems and looming natural
gas shortages seemed to leave no other alternative (Los Angeles has already ruled that no more conventional power
plants may be built in its area).

Most suitable sites for nuclear plants in arid California are
along the seacoast, for power plants require enormous quantities of cooling water. Yet the San Andreas fault zone runs up
and down nearly the whole length of the California coast. A
defeat for the company at Bodega Head might mean far greater
difficulty in obtaining licenses for other sites. And public opposition could be expected to redouble.

Public opposition to reactors in California has, indeed, been
reinforced. Reactors proposed for other California sites have
run into strong opposition. The reactor proposed for Malibu
found knowledgeable and well-organized public resistance. A
similar pattern is being repeated at the Diablo Canyon reactor
site. At Malibu, a geologic situation similar to that at Bodega
has been discovered — old faults traverse the site — and the
AEC has again asked for consideration of ground displacement
at the site. The Los Angeles Department of Water and Power,
at this writing, is still considering whether to try again with a
"novel design concept" or to abandon the site.

Despite continual difficulties, however, the reactor program
in California is struggling forward. The most spectacular event
has been the announcement of plans by the Los Angeles Department of Water and Power, and other groups, to construct
two huge reactors on a man-made island just off the Orange

County shore, in one of the most populous areas of the state, just 24 miles from Los Angeles' Civic Center. The two plants jointly will produce six times as much power as the Bodega reactor would have, and will also produce 150 million gallons of fresh water from sea water each day for Los Angeles. The project is being conducted jointly with, and partly financed by, the Atomic Energy Commission and the Department of Interior's Office of Saline Water. Congress has recently made available $72 million in federal funds for the project. The remainder of the project's $4.5 million cost will be borne by the local community. Soaring costs have dampened the original enthusiasm for this project, however, and some of the participants have apparently withdrawn.

In view of the continuing California reactor program, it may be worthwhile to take a closer look at the possibilities for accident in the now defunct Bodega plant. The best analysis of accident potential in a nuclear reactor is contained in a study of the Bodega plant in the April 1964 issue of *Nuclear Information,* by Lindsay Mattison and Richard Daly.[10] The following account is drawn largely from that report.

The Bodega reactor was to have been of the boiling-water variety being marketed by General Electric. Cooling water would be drawn in from Bodega Bay and passed into the reactor; steam at high temperature and pressure would be drawn directly from the reactor core and carried through some 200 feet of pipe to the turbines and generator in an adjoining building, where the electrical power would actually be produced. The 529 uranium fuel tubes in the reactor core would be protected from the water by metal jackets, and contained in a steel reactor vessel through which the water would flow. A pear-shaped steel drywell would provide a protective container for the reactor vessel, and the drywell in turn would be hooped with the circular pressure suppression system. In case of an accident, steam from the reactor vessel would pass through eight pipes into the pressure suppression pool, preventing undue strain on the drywell.

During a violent earthquake, the reactor building might be damaged, and one or several of the numerous pipes leading from the reactor core out of the drywell could be smashed. One possible spot for such a break would be the steam pipe leading to the turbines. If the accident also ruptured the pipes carrying coolant to the core and simultaneously rendered emergency cooling mechanisms inoperative, the result would be the rapid melting of the reactor's fuel.

This melting would occur whether the reactor were operating at the time or not. If the reactor were operating, the temperature of the fuel at full power would quickly rise past the melting point through the energy being liberated by nuclear fissioning. If the reactor were to be shut down in time, a meltdown would still result although more slowly, because of the heat derived from breakdown of the radioactive waste products accumulated in the fuel.

"The maximum accident seen by P. G. & E. as possible at its Bodega Reactor," according to Mattison and Daly, "would release 80 million curies of fission products, but contain them in the drywell." A curie is the radioactive equivalent of a gram of radium. Eighty million curies is a staggering quantity — a Hiroshima-size atomic bomb would release only a few hundred thousand curies. "The findings of various geologists point to the possibility that the reactor drywell container would be breached by on-site earth movement in the event of an earthquake, releasing fission products to the atmosphere. What would be the effect on people in the area if all 80 million curies did disperse?"

Neither Mattison and Daly, nor anyone else, consider the dispersal of such catastrophic quantities of radioactive material to be likely. Even under the conditions of a violent earthquake beneath the plant, it is hard to see how all of this material could be dispersed over a large area. Most of it is in solid or liquid form, even at the temperatures of a reactor meltdown. Only a very violent explosion could disperse this material in small enough particles for it to be borne by the wind. Since the reactor vessel would have been surrounded not only by a drywell, but also by a reactor building, the explosion would have had literally to demolish both drywell and building. Even a building cracked and distorted by an earthquake, even one that had collapsed over the reactor, would act to trap a large portion of the radioactivity.

A more likely, if still improbable, circumstance, would be the slow release of the gaseous portion of the reactor's accumulated radioactivity. A slow leakage of radiation from an earthquake-damaged reactor would result in smaller exposures to radiation over longer periods of time than the accident which is described below. An accident which resulted in even one percent of the releases assumed in what follows, although still unlikely, is not to be dismissed lightly.

In the event that winds on Bodega Head blew to the East and Northeast, an unlikely but possible situation, the following exposures could occur. In the town of Bodega Bay, some two miles from the reactor, nearly everyone would die the first day.

For those without shelter the external gamma radiation exposure could rise to 3,120 rads the first day and 14,000 rads could be accumulated in the following 90 days. The AEC suggests half of any population exposed to 350 to 500 rads will die within a week. . . . Some twenty miles from the site, the city of Santa Rosa has 31,000 residents. There, exposures could be 72 rads the first day and some 4,600 rads in 90 days. From inhalation while the cloud passes, the beta radiation to the lungs could be 320 rads the first day and 960 the first week. Thyroid doses from inhalation in Santa Rosa could be 4,700 rads. The Federal Radiation Council recommends that for the general population a thyroid dose of .5 rads *yearly* should not be exceeded. . . .

For the San Francisco metropolitan area — fifty miles from the reactor — the external doses could be 15 rads on the first day and 104 in 90 days. The lung dose could be 84 and 250 rads, for the first day and week respectively. The thyroid dose could be 1240 rads. . . .

One may conclude that people within five miles downwind of the reactor would probably be killed and within twenty miles many of the people exposed would be very sick. Beyond that distance a few would be sick within the first week and such long term effects as increased leukemia, thyroid cancer, and congenital malformations would eventually make their appearance. For distances of hundreds of miles from such a release of radioactivity the AEC . . . suggests, "Probable destruction of standing crops, restrictions on agriculture for the first year." [11]

These predictions are based on calculation techniques developed in an AEC study of the consequences of reactor accidents, and assume a number of pessimistic weather conditions, such as thermal inversions (where a layer of cold air is trapped under a warmer one) and steady winds. The AEC has recently published more elaborate methods for calculating the effects of such an accident, but the Mattison and Daly study remains substantially accurate.

The accident which is assumed for these calculations is quite unlikely under normal conditions. Certainly the populations at risk would be evacuated within hours. For such an accident to occur, the normal water cooling of the reactor must be shut off, and the emergency cooling systems must all fail to function. In addition, the various devices for containing radioactivity from the reactor core must fail to function effectively — the reactor vessel, drywell, and pressure suppression pool, as well as the reactor building itself. Whether all these things would happen during an earthquake at the reactor site itself is a matter for speculation, but it seems at least conceivable. As we pointed out earlier, even if an accident were to occur, the actual releases of radioactivity are not likely to be as great as those assumed for the study. As Dr. Quaide pointed out, the decision in such circumstances is a moral one: If there is even a slight chance of danger, should we go ahead and build the plant?

This is a decision which will have to be faced more and more frequently in California. Because of the state's air pollution and fuel problems, most future power plants are expected to be nuclear, and because of cooling-water requirements will be sited on the earthquake-prone coast. A virtual rerun of the Bodega dispute is already going on at Malibu in Los Angeles County, where a complex of four reactors has been proposed by the Los Angeles Department of Water and Power. The first reactor, half again as large as the Bodega plant was to be, was scheduled for operation in 1968, but public opposition and difficulties in licensing have already pushed that date farther into the future.

As at Bodega, opposition to the plant at first centered on conservation issues, providing a context of debate in which safety problems appeared and then predominated. A group called Malibu Citizens for Conservation was formed and achieved a membership of more than 1000 (the 1964 population of Malibu was only 9000). On January 29, 1963, the Department of Water and Power submitted their proposal for the first Malibu plant to the AEC. By the end of 1964, the failure of the Bodega project, the Alaskan earthquake, and a dam disaster in nearby Baldwin Hills all lent impetus to the citizens' group opposing the reactor, and an impressive array of scientific and technical advice and evidence was marshaled.

The reactor was to be built in a beautiful coast location, Corral Canyon; a brochure from the Department of Water and Power describes it this way: "The site is sheltered on three sides by the canyon's surrounding terrain rising 650 feet above the canyon floor. The fourth side faces the ocean, which is across U.S. Highway 101. . . . The nuclear power station will be attractively designed with good architecture and landscape to provide a pleasing appearance." [12]

The protective sound of those high canyon walls is misleading, however. Consulting geologist Thomas L. Bailey reported to the citizens' group: ". . . the proposed site for a Nuclear Reactor Plant in lower Corral Canyon is a geologically unstable area subject to severe landsliding. . . ." [13] Closer examination revealed even more disturbing aspects of the site. Dr. Thomas Clements, for thirty years head of the Department of Geology at the University of Southern California, reported:

It is the opinion of the undersigned that the lower part of Corral Canyon is crossed by a large overthrust fault. As a result, the rocks of this area are highly fractured, crushed and squeezed and, therefore, are weak and unstable. . . . the writer recommends that the site be abandoned.[14]

Dr. Barclay Kamb, Professor of Geology and Geophysics, California Institute of Technology, after making a comprehensive survey of the site, concluded:

> The disturbed zone at Corral Canyon passes directly beneath the proposed reactor installation. . . . In relation to the possible range of exposure to fault hazards in Southern California, the Corral Canyon site ranks as among the more hazardous possible.[15]

These geologists and others submitted their opinions to the Los Angeles Department of Water and Power (LADWP), but with little effect. In July of 1964 they were submitted to the Los Angeles County Board of Supervisors, which was being asked to reverse the granting of a zoning exception for the plant. The Board was also presented with a report from the LADWP's own consultant, Dr. Richard Jahns, then Dean of the School of Earth Sciences, Stanford University. Dr. Jahns stated:

> In this writer's opinion, the possibility of fault movement within the site area during the planned life of the power station is remote. With the understanding that the reactors and other critical structures would be engineered for appropriate earthquake resistance and that *none of them would be placed across a recognizable fault,* it is also this writer's opinion that the site is a satisfactory one . . . [emphasis added].[16]

The Board of Supervisors unanimously denied the zone exception for the power plant, stating that

> In the face of these conflicting reports . . . it appears that no one can predict with any certainty what degree of safety could or would be built into the Atomic plant. . . . We cannot, in good

conscience, approve such an action which may result in dire consequences, including the possibility of loss of many lives.[17]

There is some question as to whether the LADWP requires a zone exception in order to build its plants, and the utility has announced its intention to proceed in the face of the County Supervisors' opposition. The Supervisors countered by passing a resolution to intervene in the Atomic Energy Commission proceedings regarding licensing of the plant.

Dr. Jahns's report has recently reappeared in the controversy, however. In pronouncing the site satisfactory so long as there were no faults underlying the reactor itself, he foreshadowed the most serious difficulty which the utility would encounter. During excavation, a fault running through the reactor site itself was discovered. The situation was then precisely comparable to that at Bodega. The utility maintained that the fault was inactive and had suffered no movement for at least 10,000 years; the citizens' group maintained that slippage on the fault could very well occur during the lifetime of the reactor.

Again, the Atomic Energy Commission expressed its doubts about the design of the plant in the presence of a fault. After a long series of hearings and reviews, in March 1967 the AEC insisted that the LADWP resubmit its application, showing a design which would protect the reactor against ground displacement. Despite their own consultant's report which insisted that no reactor would be placed across a fault, the LADWP has indicated it has no plans to move the plant. "We can design for ground displacement," a utility official told a trade publication. "There's nothing hard about that." Pacific Gas and Electric had ducked the issue by withdrawing their application. The Los Angeles utility has apparently decided to face it at Malibu. "Anywhere you go in California," the LADWP official told the reporter, "you usually have a fault. Moving [the reactor] won't buy you anything." [18]

This gloomy estimate has been confirmed by a Department of Interior study of another LADWP reactor site, Bolsa Island, where LADWP and private utilities plan to build the two huge power and fresh-water plants for the Los Angeles area. The Bolsa Island project also has a long history.

In July of 1964, President Johnson directed the Secretary of the Interior, in cooperation with the Atomic Energy Commission, to develop a program for the large-scale desalting of sea water. On September 22, the Secretary's report was delivered to the President and on April 5, 1965, he submitted legislation to Congress accompanied by a message which expressed what seemed to be his strong and continuing interest in accelerated efforts to increase the country's supply of fresh water. Johnson asked for a five-year extension of the current water-desalting program and an increase in funding of $200 million over that period; the program covered a wide range of research and development problems, but gave heavy emphasis to the possibility of using very large nuclear reactors in dual-purpose plants for desalination and the production of electric power. The program was passed by Congress with little change, and on September 2, 1965, President Johnson announced, while dedicating a dam at Summersville, West Virginia, "The Administration has just asked Congress' approval to share in constructing the world's largest nuclear-fueled desalting and electric power plant in the Los Angeles area."

Sea water can be turned into fresh water simply by distilling it. More than 800 plants are in operation throughout the world, turning sea or brackish water into fresh water, most of them operating on this simple principle in one form or another. The problem is cost — it takes a great deal of heat energy to boil water, and energy from coal or atoms is expensive. One way around the cost difficulty is to build very large nuclear plants, which also produce electricity and in which the unit cost of power drops as the plants get larger.

In April of 1964 an Office of Science and Technology task force headed by Dr. Roger Revelle reported to the President that if nuclear plants were sufficiently large, and were used for both power production and desalination, the combined savings would allow fresh water costs low enough to compete with natural supplies in some areas.[19]

The eventual result of that report was the Bolsa Island proposal: two reactors which would between them produce as much power as the Hoover Dam, 1,800,000 kilowatts, and 150,000,000 gallons of water per day — enough for a city the size of San Francisco. Clearly, there are very few places in the country which could absorb such an installation, and where water scarcity and cost could make it useful. The Los Angeles area was seemingly ideal, but unfortunately had already committed itself to a multibillion dollar system to bring water through aqueducts from Northern California. According to Frank Di Luzio, then Director of the Office of Saline Water, testifying before a House subcommittee, the Los Angeles complex would not have considered the desalting plant for another decade without considerable federal encouragement.[20] This has taken the form of a more than $72 million subsidy for the $400 million installation, the remainder of the cost to be borne by the Los Angeles Department of Water and Power, the Metropolitan Water District, the San Diego Gas and Electric Company, and the Southern California Edison Company. Actual costs of the project are now estimated at $750 million, far greater than original guesses, and the fate of the plant is again in question.

If the Los Angeles area was ideal for the project in one way, it was a problem in others. The sprawling nature of the city would force a reactor installation quite far away if it were not to be built in a heavily populated district, and the costs of transporting water and power would be great.

For economic purposes therefore, an ideal location for the plant is a man-made island to be built 3500 feet from the shore of Orange County and 24 miles from the heart of Los Angeles. This puts the plant close to its market; whether it takes it far enough away from the people is another question. The serious problem of whether a man-made island will be a reasonable foundation for a nuclear plant in the earthquake-ridden area also remains open to question. A recent Interior Department survey of the site recommends taking into account the possibility of ground displacement on the site during an earthquake. The moral question which the utilities faced at Bodega and Malibu will be faced again to a greater or lesser extent at Bolsa Island. Can even the small risk of catastrophic accident which is unavoidable in the present state of technology be accepted?

This question is growing more critical, as the number and size of nuclear plants planned for California grow. Sites for nuclear plants have been purchased in Mendocino County, Point Arena, Montezuma Slough, South Moss Landing, sites just north of San Diego and south of Sacramento, Nipomo Dunes, Diablo Canyon, Cayucos Beach, as well as Malibu and Bolsa Island; Southern California Edison has recently announced plans for a $200 million nuclear generating facility in Santa Barbara, California, north of Los Angeles; the plant will generate 1,000,000 kilowatts. Reactors are already operating at Vallecitos, San Onofre, and Humboldt Bay; other projects will probably have been announced by the time these words are printed. Unfortunately, California utilities, both public and private, seem to have decided the question to their own satisfaction. There has been little public discussion of the various alternative solutions to California's growing air pollution and fuel and water problems.

If citizens' groups opposed to reactors learned many lessons in the battle of Bodega Bay, so did the utilities. Pacific Gas and Electric, still smarting after its loss at Bodega, led the way in establishing procedures for heading off controversy, and has so far been succeeding quite well. Recognizing that organized public opposition generally centers around conservation groups, P. G. & E., when it proposed to build a reactor at its site on Nipomo Dunes, a beautiful area on the coast just south of San Luis Obispo, met first with the most influential of California's conservation organizations, the Sierra Club.

Some members of the Sierra Club's Board of Directors felt strongly about preserving the natural beauty of Nipomo Dunes, and the Board assured P. G. & E. there would be opposition to a nuclear power plant there. A compromise was eventually reached, in which the Board voted not to oppose a reactor at another P. G. & E. site, Diablo Canyon, a few miles to the north, if the utility would scrap the Nopomo Dunes plan. P. G. & E. then went on to gain the acquiescence of a number of other conservation groups to the Diablo Canyon site, and simultaneously worked through a special task force to gain state acceptance through the State Resources Agency. According to P. G. & E. President Sibley, "Advance cooperation with governmental agencies, responsible conservation interests and other segments of society brings out points of difference at an early date. . . . We feel strongly that . . . this is very much a part of advance planning." [21] Sibley was quoted as referring to the granting of State and AEC approvals for the San Onofre plant without "headline problems" as attesting to the success of this approach.

The greatest success has been in gaining state and local government acquiescence. In fact P. G. & E. and the State Resources Agency, a government coordinating agency, after a joint meeting in the summer of 1964, established a joint task force to secure prior state approval of the utility's plans. This approach was soon copied by other California utilities interested in reactor development. "I'm not aware of any utility not being enthusiastic about the role of this sitting committee," stated the chairman of the task force, Harold D. Bissell.[22]

Government cooperation is only half the story, however. The government-utility task force early came to an agreement on the Malibu reactor site which is nevertheless now being hotly contested. "The public doesn't always see it our way," said Bissell.[23]

The public apparently doesn't see it their way at Diablo Canyon, either. Despite the efforts of Pacific Gas and Electric to line up conservation groups in advance, a storm is brewing over this site. Opposition is being led by the Scenic Shoreline Preservation Conference, Inc., which formed around a minority of the Sierra Club's Board of Directors who disagreed with the decision to trade Diablo Canyon for Nipomo Dunes. The group is headquartered in Santa Barbara, which is itself shortly to be the site of another large nuclear installation: California utilities may apparently expect continuing opposition.

Nor is California the only area in the country where reactors have been greeted with public opposition. On December 10, 1962, the Consolidated Edison Company of New York applied to the Atomic Energy Commission for a license to construct a 700,000 kilowatt reactor (twice the size of the proposed Bodega plant) in the heart of New York City. The reactor was to be in the Ravenswood district of Queens on the shore of the East River, just opposite Manhattan at 72nd Street. The proposal for the "Ravenswood Reactor" drew a fire of criticism, led by the Scientists' Committee for Radiation Information. In one of its reports the group stated, "Although the probability of a serious nuclear accident may be very low, it should be emphasized that major accidents in nuclear facilities differ qualitatively from those in conventional industrial facilities. A major accident in a conventional industrial facility would not contaminate a large area with long-lived, highly potent toxicants. By contrast, a nuclear reactor produces the most toxic contaminants . . . [an accident] would be a catastrophe of staggering proportions. . . .

"The foregoing considerations could be overlooked if the reactor were to be located in a remote region. They are issues of paramount importance, however, when a public utility plans to construct a reactor in a huge metropolitan district." [24]

David Lilienthal, past Chairman of the Atomic Energy Commission, commented more succinctly on this proposal to put a reactor into one of the most densely populated areas on earth. According to the *New York Times*, he called it "a very risky business." [25] An ordinance barring reactors from the city was introduced before the City Council. In the face of the growing and articulate opposition, and with the likelihood of difficulty in obtaining the requisite AEC approval, Con Ed withdrew its proposal; the reason publicly given was that power could be obtained more cheaply via long-distance transmission lines from hydroelectric stations in Labrador.

The same utility has suffered difficulties over another nuclear plant 24 miles north of New York City on the bank of the Hudson River, the Indian Point No. 2 plant, at the same site where Con Edison has been operating the far smaller Indian Point No. 1 reactor since 1962. (Although now operating reliably, this first plant was plagued by operating difficulties and unanticipated costs during its first years of operation; the Public Utilities Commission has recently been asked to consider whether Con Ed showed faulty judgment in building it.) The second plant has been opposed by local conservation groups, and suit has been filed against the Con Ed Board of Directors for allegedly gambling the utility's resources on an untried and uncertain technology.

A number of other controversies have arisen across the country. The most spectacular of all battles was the struggle over the Enrico Fermi Atomic Power Plant in Lagoona Beach, Michigan, near Detroit. The governor of Michigan, a leading senator, labor unions and citizens groups were united in opposition to the reactor; litigation eventually reached the Supreme Court, which in a divided decision sided with the reactor proponents. The plant was constructed, but never operated properly, and finally, in October 1966, suffered a near-disastrous accident which may have put it permanently out of commission.

Despite such scattered opposition, the nuclear power program has recently undergone enormous expansion. Beginning in 1965, a trickle of orders from utilities turned quickly into a flood which by the end of 1967 showed no sign of abating. In 1966, twenty-one new, large nuclear power stations were ordered; in 1967, the number of new orders had jumped to 32. Most of these plants would be in the range of 800,000 to 1,100,000 kilowatts, five times the size of the largest reactors then in operation. By the middle of 1968, more than 100 nuclear power plants were being planned, but only 12 privately owned plants were in commercial operation, all but two of them smaller than 200,000 kilowatts.

As we have seen, this flood of orders has taken even the nuclear industry by surprise, for only fairly recently it seemed that the difficulty of assuring safety and reliability in nuclear plants might make them commercial impossibilities.

IV

THE PROBLEM OF INSURANCE

ASSURING SAFETY has been an obstacle to commercial nuclear power since the early days of the program. On March 22, 1957, Harold Vance, Acting Chairman of the Atomic Energy Commission, sent a letter to Carl Durham, Chairman of the Joint Congressional Committee on Atomic Energy. Enclosed with the letter was an advance copy of a study done by the AEC which would soon be famous. The report was titled, "Theoretical Possibilities and Consequences of Major Accidents in Large Nuclear Power Plants," and was based on research done at the AEC's Brookhaven National Laboratory under the direction of Kenneth W. Downes. It was an attempt to predict the damage which would be done to the public should a major reactor accident occur. "Since the beginning of the reactor program," Vance said in his letter, "the experts and the Congress and the public and the [Atomic Energy] Commission have all been concerned with the causes and the possible magnitude of damage from reactor accidents and with means of prevention." [1]

The study, which is now generally known simply by its AEC document number, "WASH-740," focuses on what was in 1957 considered to be a "typical" reactor of the near future — one about half the size of the proposed Bodega reactor, and a sixth of the size of most plants now being planned. "The reactor is assumed to be located near a large body of water, most likely a river, about 30 miles from a major city." The Acting Chairman of the AEC summarized the report in the following way:

> For the three types of assumed accidents, the theoretical estimates indicated that personal damage might range from a lower limit of none injured or killed to an upper limit, in the worst case, of 3400 killed and about 43,000 injured.
>
> Theoretical property damages ranged from a lower limit of about one half million dollars to an upper limit in the worst case of about seven billion dollars. This latter figure is largely due to assumed contamination of land with fission products.
>
> Under adverse combinations of the conditions considered, it was estimated that people could be killed at distances up to 15 miles, and injured at distances of about 45 miles. Land contamination could extend for greater distances.
>
> In the large majority of theoretical accidents considered, the total assumed losses would not exceed a few hundred million dollars.[2]

Although this report is now more than ten years old, its conclusions are still important. In 1965 the AEC reexamined the study, in the light of the somewhat different and far larger reactors then being planned. A letter from the Chairman of the Atomic Energy Commission to the Joint Committee on Atomic Energy, dated June 18, 1965, refers to the new research, and although insisting that the likelihood of a serious accident was even lower than it had been in 1957, concludes that "the theoretically calculated damages [of such an accident] would not be less and under some circumstances would be substantially more than the consequences reported in the earlier study."[3]

The nature and details of the AEC's new study are not known, for despite persistent rumors that a whole new report updating WASH-740 had been prepared (the forthcoming report had even been publicly referred to by one of the Commissioners[4]), nothing has been released, nor did Chairman Seaborg give the basis for the remarks in his letter. The "circumstances" under which still more serious accidents might happen are therefore unknown.

The original WASH-740 attempted to define the likelihood, as well as the severity, of a disastrous accident. The following surprising statement is made: "Nuclear reactors have been operated since December 2, 1942, with a remarkable safety record."[5] a footnote amplifies this remark: "All the half-dozen 'runaway' incidents (Chalk River, Borax, EBR-1, etc.) experienced thus far, either inadvertent or planned, have occurred in research or experimental test reactors — in contrast to the steadily operating power reactors considered here."

This footnote provides the only mention in the entire 105-page report of accidents which had already occurred. It is even misleading. *All* the reactors built in this country at the time the report appeared, and which were for the purpose of generating electricity, were experimental. They are listed by the AEC in its annual summary of the reactor program under the heading "Experimental Reactor Systems." None of these, nor any other civilian reactors in the U.S. at the time, could be characterized as "steadily operating": at the time the report was published, three of the six reactors in civilian use had already been shut down.[6]

The report goes on to say: "This record of safety, although highly reassuring, does not afford a dependable statistical basis for estimating the probability of occurrence of serious reactor accidents in the future." WASH-740's authors therefore proceeded to solicit the guesses of an unnamed group of "outstanding leaders in reactor technology and associated fields" as to the likelihood of a major accident. These anonymous experts' estimates ranged "from one chance in 100,000 to one in a billion per year for each reactor." Despite this reassuring opinion, the report goes on to list some of the factors which might lead to a serious accident:

1. Many power reactor systems will operate under high pressures. High pressure systems are subject to failure.

2. The cumulative effect of radiation on physical and chemical properties of materials, after long periods of time, is largely unknown.

3. Various metals used in reactors such as uranium, aluminum, zirconium, sodium and beryllium, under certain conditions not at present clearly understood, may react explosively with water, also present in many reactors . . . Chemical reactions of enough violence to rupture the containment vessels, with release of fission products, could occur.

4. After initial operation, many of the vital components become inaccessible for inspections. In non-nuclear plants, serious accidents are often averted through detection of incipient failure.

5. Much remains to be learned about the characteristics of nuclear systems.[7]

Nothing at all is said about human error, the principal or contributing cause of all the accidents which had already occurred, and something which could be expected with certainty to continue as a permanent and major hazard. Another serious omission is a class of hazards which were, and remain, the most grave in the reactor program. These are the special hazards associated with a particular design, the liquid-metal-cooled fast reactor. This latter omission is surprising, in view of the fact that the first commercial prototype of this kind of reactor was, at the time of the report's appearance, receiving enormous amounts of publicity. This was the Enrico Fermi Atomic Power Plant near Detroit, Michigan, of which we will have more to say in a later chapter.

The report is therefore weakened by the omission of the worst classes of reactor hazards, the absence of any discussion of past accidents, and the inclusion of anonymous but optimistic guesses as to the unlikeliness of a reactor accident occurring. In this light, the drastic damage estimates produced appear still more disturbing.

WASH-740 appeared at a critical point in the reactor program. The Atomic Energy Act of 1954 had stated as one of its purposes "a program to encourage widespread participation in the development and utilization of atomic energy for peaceful purposes. . . ." The participation that was to be encouraged was that of private industry, and in fact the little-debated 1954 Atomic Energy law was prepared largely in response to widespread feeling that the Government should relax its total monopoly of the industry. Under the Eisenhower Administration, in 1953, the Joint Congressional Committee on Atomic Energy held extensive hearings on "Atomic Power Development and Private Enterprise." The Atomic Energy Commission came in for severe criticism at this time for not having pursued the peaceful applications of atomic energy more vigorously, and a general feeling emerged that the cost-cutting abilities of private industry would soon produce economic nuclear electric power. Both Republican and Democratic spokesmen testified that it was time to turn over to free enterprise at least part of the "nationalized" atomic energy industry.

Legislation permitting private enterprise in the nuclear field had been drafted during the Truman Administration, but had not got off the ground. Encouraging private industry to enter the nuclear field was entirely in accord with the objectives of the Eisenhower Administration, however, which had committed itself to keeping the government out of the power business wherever possible, and to an Atoms for Peace program. In 1953, Eisenhower appointed investment banker Lewis L. Strauss Chairman of the Atomic Energy Commission; Strauss had been a member of the first Commission and Eisenhower's personal advisor on atomic energy affairs. In his autobiography,[8] Strauss describes his own opposition to federal involvement in electric power production (a principle which was later to make him a major figure in the Dixon-Yates dispute).

Chemical and manufacturing firms were understandably eager to capitalize on the enormous investments in atomic energy they had made through military programs; in some cases these investments of manpower and resources were made quite involuntarily. General Leslie R. Groves, head of the Manhattan Engineer District, describes the persuasion that was necessary to induce the Du Pont Corporation to manage construction of the plutonium production reactors built during the Second World War, and afterwards, a massive and enormously risky project for which Du Pont received no compensation beyond expenses.[9]

Other industrial companies, on the other hand, which were not participating in the government's secret research programs in atomic power production, were afraid of being excluded from what everyone was sure would eventually be a huge and lucrative industry. The manufacturers and prospective manufacturers of reactors were therefore eager for the freeing of atomic energy from federal domination. The only difficulty was in finding customers for privately manufactured reactors. Normally conservative utility companies were very reluctant to embark on this still uncharted sea of nuclear energy.

Admiral Strauss describes in his autobiography the early attempts he made to persuade privately owned power companies to participate in the reactor program. His efforts met their first success when he persuaded the Duquesne Power and Light Company to join with the AEC in construction of the first nuclear plant to produce commercial power. Most of the risk was borne by the AEC, which paid for, owned, and operated the nuclear portion of the plant, at Shippingport, Pennsylvania. It went into operation in December of 1957.

This first AEC venture was followed by a dozen projects involving varying degrees of federal assistance. Privately owned utilities received design assistance, and indirect subsidies in fuel costs and waste disposal services. Publicly owned utilities received direct assistance in construction funds. The most spectacular and controversial of the attempts to build reactors with private funds, the Enrico Fermi plant near Detroit, seemed to be foundering in 1957 in a wave of protests and legal difficulties involving the safety of such plants.

The question of safety was, in fact, closely tied to that of private utility participation. By 1957, Windscale, Chalk River, and other incidents had brought home the fact that reactor accidents could happen.

A serious reactor accident would cause extensive damage to persons and property far from the reactor itself — damage for which the owner of the reactor would almost certainly be liable. The WASH-740 report gives some idea of what such damage could amount to. No public or private utility could face the prospects of such catastrophic loss. In a report accompanying the Price-Anderson Act, which will be discussed shortly, the Joint Committee on Atomic Energy stated: "It was brought to the attention of the Joint Committee in the 1956 hearings, which the Joint Committee is required to hold under section 202 of the Atomic Energy Act of 1954, that the problem of possible liability in connection with the operation of reactors is a major deterrent to further industrial participation in the program . . . the problem of liability has become a major roadblock." [10]

The Joint Committee immediately set about trying to remove the roadblock. The problem was to find insurance adequate to cover the risks of reactor operation; the first step was obviously to establish the nature of the risks. On July 6, 1956, the Joint Committee asked the AEC to establish the outside limits of such risks; the eventual response to this request was WASH-740, published almost a year later. But the Joint Committee did not wait to see the study they had requested. Hearings were begun in May of 1956, to which representatives of the atomic energy industry and insurance industry were invited; a unique piece of legislation, the Price-Anderson Act, was introduced by the Committee later in the year. Congress failed to act that year on the bill, however, and hearings continued in 1957.

The problem was simply that insurance companies politely but firmly declined to insure reactors for anything like the full amount of risk. Testifying before the Joint Committee, several insurance company executives made the point that there was simply not enough experience with reactors to make normal insurance possible; since no estimate of the likelihood of an accident could be made, the insurance companies could have no basis on which to issue a policy. The potential risk was far greater than any ever assumed before. One insurance executive put it quite strongly:

> The catastrophe hazard is apparently many times as great as anything previously known in industry and therefore poses a major challenge to insurance companies. . . . We have heard estimates of catastrophe potential under the worst possible circumstances running not merely into millions or tens of millions but into hundreds of millions and billions of dollars.

> It is a reasonable question of public policy as to whether a hazard of this magnitude should be permitted, if it actually exists. Obviously there is no principle of insurance which can be applied to a single location where the potential loss approaches such astronomical proportions. Even if insurance could be found, there is a serious question whether the amount of damage to persons and property would be worth the possible benefit accruing from atomic development.[11]

The Joint Committee had reached an impasse; in order to have private industry participate in the reactor program, utilities would have to own and operate their own reactors. This they declined to do unless adequate insurance were available. But insurance companies refused to assume the risk.

Instead of accepting the very reasonable judgment that if reactors were uninsurable they were not ready for commercial application, the Joint Committee proposed a unique solution to their problem. In order to open the atomic energy field to "private enterprise," the Federal Government would itself provide the insurance which private companies would not. This may sound like an odd sort of free enterprise — the taxpayer assuming the risk and private industry accepting the profits. Nevertheless, in 1957, Senator Clinton Anderson and Congressman Melvin Price of the Joint Committee introduced into the Senate and House what shortly became Public Law 88–703, the "Price-Anderson Act."

This curious bill has received surprisingly little attention in the press. It provides a straightforward federal subsidy to a multibillion dollar industry. It represents an intrusion of the Federal Government into the power industry and into the insurance industry which establishes a radical precedent, and it effectively passes the risks of the reactor industry on to the taxpayer. Section 170 e. of the Atomic Energy Act is amended to read:

> The aggregate liability for a single nuclear incident (reactor accident) . . . shall not exceed the sum of $500,000,000 together with the amount of financial protection required. . . .

This means that the operator of a reactor must obtain as much private insurance as he can (the "financial protection required"). The Atomic Energy Commission will then provide $500 million of protection on top of that. (Technically, the AEC "holds harmless" the reactor operator for "public liability" up to this amount.) But by law, the reactor operator and the Federal Government *are not liable* for any damages in excess of that $500 million plus private insurance. In other words, if the WASH-740's maximum of $7 billion in property damage in a single accident were realized, only one-fourteenth of the damage would be covered. This "limitation of liability" clause assures private utilities that no matter how bad an accident is, they will not suffer any financial loss.

The law does provide, however, that utilities owning reactors must buy as much insurance privately as they can. We have already seen that insurance companies were rather reluctant to provide any insurance at all. Under considerable prodding from the Joint Committee, two combines of insurance companies were formed, one including the country's mutual insurance companies, the other including stock companies. Between them they included every major insurance company in the nation, and a third organization, the Mutual Atomic Energy Reinsurance Pool, was formed to draw on the insurance capacities of Europe. These combines, which effectively drew on all the insurance resources of the Western world, together agreed to provide up to $60 million insurance for each commercial reactor.

It is clear that this is merely a token of private insurance when measured against the government-provided $500 million. Even ten years later, despite constant urging from the Joint Committee, the insurance companies have only been willing to increase their participation to $74 million.

This faint private insurance participation is therefore overshadowed by a massive federal intrusion into the reactor industry. This subsidy not only exposes the taxpayer to risks he has heard very little about, but it allows the rapid expansion and commercial use of a technology that is simply not yet ready for commercial application. The consequence is an enormous safety hazard which would have been avoided if the atomic energy industry were forced to assume responsibility for its own risks.

The Federal Government may also be providing an indirect subsidy to private utilities; this can be judged from a comparison of the insurance premiums being paid private companies and the fees being paid the AEC. According to agreements in force in 1964, the Commonwealth Edison Company of Chicago was to pay $233,000 a year to private insurance companies for $60 million of insurance. For the $500 million protection provided by the AEC, they were to pay only one-tenth of that, $21,000, in "annual indemnity fees." The Consolidated Edison Company of New York was to pay $266,500 for their $60 million private insurance, and only $17,550 for the AEC's $500 million. The Yankee Atomic Electric Company of Boston was to pay $125,000 to private companies and $18,000 to the AEC.[12] Even accepting the greater likelihood of small accidents (which would be paid for by private insurers), the imbalance is striking.

An interesting sidelight to this is provided by the widely varying premiums charged by insurance companies for different reactors. The insurance combines maintain their own staff for evaluating individual reactor hazards, and these studies are presumably the basis of the premiums. Thus Yankee Atomic's reactor is slightly larger than Consolidated Edison's — but the premium they pay is less than half of Con Ed's for the same amount of insurance. Does this mean that the insurance combines have rated the Con Ed reactor, just 25 miles from New York, as twice as hazardous as Yankee Atomic's?

The problem of private participation in the atomic energy program has not improved since 1957, it has only grown worse. The Price-Anderson Act was originally to have run for only ten years. So important is this law for continued private participation in the reactor program that on May 26, 1965, Clinton Anderson and Melvin Price introduced bills in Congress which would extend the law for an additional ten years to 1977, even though it was then still a full two years from expiring. The

Joint Committee held extensive hearings on these bills in the summer of 1965 and discovered that the situation remained exactly as it was in 1957. Insurance companies did not want to take any larger slice of the reactor liability, and utilities would not buy reactors unless protection were provided.

Mr. DeRoy Thomas, of the Hartford Insurance Group, appeared as the principal spokesman for the insurance combines. At one point he referred to the "demand or suggestion" by the Joint Committee that private insurers increase their coverage beyond the token $60 million they were providing. The Joint Committee was asking the insurers to bring their insurance up to $100 million. After canvassing the few companies which were not already part of the nuclear combine, Thomas reported to the committee that 19 new members had been found and that the combines would increase their coverage — to $74 million. The Chairman of the Joint Committee pressed Thomas on this point. He testified that all available insurance capacity had been used.

Chairman Holifield: Do you have foreign participation in this?

Mr. Thomas: We do, sir.

Holifield: Lloyd's of London?

Thomas: Yes, sir. It goes past that. I think the only capacity we have refused was a small piece tendered to us from the Odessa pool.[13]

If the insurance companies were adamant about not making any substantial increase in their coverage, the numerous private utility representatives at the hearings testified over and over that they would hesitate before buying new reactors, and might even cancel contracts they had already signed, if government indemnity under Price-Anderson were not extended. Mel Frankel, a nuclear engineer appearing on behalf of the Los Angeles Department of Water and Power, one of the biggest reactor customers in the country, testified:

> Without the protection, which presently is provided by the Price-Anderson Act, it is doubtful that any utility would consider it prudent to build nuclear plants.[14]

Mr. Frankel also testified that the Department of Water and Power had inserted a clause in its contract to build the Malibu reactor that would allow it to terminate the contract in the event that government or private insurance was not available. "We understand that this provision is standard in most similar contracts," he stated.

This testimony is not reassuring about the confidence of electric utilities in the safety of the reactors they are purchasing in such great numbers. WASH-740, with its ominous projections, is apparently carefully read by utility executives. Price-Anderson shifts the burden of concern from the utilities to the Government, however, and the reactor program continues to expand.

One hundred or so reactors are now planned or are under construction; only a dozen are now in operation. This handful of power plants has a spotty record at best; nearly all of them are only a fraction of the size of the reactors planned for the coming years. The new reactors will not only be three to six times larger than anything with which there has been past experience, but they will be far closer to population centers. This increase in size and decrease in distance from people constitutes an enormous increase in the potential hazard from the plants, a hazard which will continue to increase as the momentum of the reactor industry gathers.

The larger a reactor is, the more economical it is. Nuclear reactors do not begin to compete with coal-fueled plants until their capacity is larger than 500,000 kilowatts. In low-cost coal areas, reactors don't compete until they produce about 1,000,-000 kilowatts — more than half the power capacity of the Hoover Dam. Thus, to go on selling reactors, the manufacturers (principally GE and Westinghouse, although Babcock and Wilcox, and Combustion Engineering have recently entered the field) must build ever larger reactors.

This increase in size brings with it a host of new problems. As we have seen, the most serious kind of reactor accident is one in which the fuel melts — either because the flow of cooling water has been shut off, or because there has been a failure of the controls which keep the chain reaction within bounds (a "runaway"). Such a "meltdown" is dangerous because it releases the enormously poisonous fission products, or radioactive wastes, ordinarily locked in the reactor fuel. If the heating or runaway of the reactor is sudden enough, the result could be an explosion, or the heating may result in further chemical explosions. A sufficiently violent explosion would break open the reactor container, with the consequent release of the radioactive wastes into the atmosphere. It is the drifting of such a cloud of radioactive poison which is assumed to cause the kind of damage cited in WASH-740. In that report, the worst accident postulated was one in which only half of the fission products accumulated in the reactor fuel were released.

The present approach to forestalling such an accident is to

provide all the devices which can be thought of to prevent it: to design the reactor core itself, as far as possible, so that no "runaways" can occur; and then, in case all else fails, to surround the whole reactor with a dome, generally called a "containment sphere" in the jargon of the trade. In some designs, as at Bodega, the containment sphere is replaced by a "pressure-suppression" system which acts as a safety valve to bleed off pressure before it reaches explosive proportions. The trend toward larger reactors has made this straightforward-seeming approach even more difficult than it was when WASH-740 was issued. Clifford K. Beck spoke in February 1965 at a meeting of the American Nuclear Society; he was at the time deputy director of regulation for the Atomic Energy Commission. In talking about the new problems which were appearing in the new reactors, he said,

> Let me just mention one technical fact to point up the significance of the changes that are occurring. There is a very large difference in the implications of a major meltdown in a [1,000,000-kilowatt reactor — the size which was then being planned] as contrasted to that in a [100,000 kilowatt reactor — roughly the size which was typical at the time of WASH-740]. For the small reactor, it may make good sense to surround it with a leak-proof, concrete "thermos bottle" containment, and, in the case of accident, just walk away and let everything inside settle down and cool off. For the [1,000,000-kilowatt] reactor . . . if you walk away from that "thermos-bottle," its temperature curve, after perhaps a momentary decline, will rise continuously and will simply heat up until it bursts, so a reliable cooling system must be added.[15]

In the past it had been possible to say, "No matter what happens in the reactor, even if all the safety devices fail, there is always the containment sphere to keep radiation from drifting into populated areas." Now the whole picture has changed.

Because of the greatly enlarged size of reactors, the containment is no longer sufficient in and of itself to prevent hazard to the public. *Both* the safety devices and the containment have to function. As Beck pointed out, "the necessity of other systems working, besides just the containment vessels, becomes more urgent."

The "other systems" which must work are mostly emergency cooling systems, such as high-pressure water sprays, to keep the temperatures down after an accident has happened. Because of the ever present danger of error on the part of those operating the reactor, and because reactor behavior is still not entirely understood, the potential *causes* of an accident can never be entirely eliminated, and this is well recognized. Safety measures to counteract the effects of a serious accident which results in the melting of the reactor fuel must therefore be instituted. The point of these measures is simply to protect the public, and as reactors move more and more closely to cities, the importance of these measures increases.

In the early days of the reactor program, each application to the Atomic Energy Commission for a license to build a reactor contained a "Hazards Summary" which was essentially divided into two sections. The first described the measures the applicant, an electric utility, was to take to prevent serious accidents. This section contained a number of what were called "credible accidents," each being a description of what would happen in the case of a foreseeable mishap, such as predictable operator errors or mechanical failures. In each case the safety devices which would prevent such a mishap from turning into a major accident with release of radioactivity were described. A "maximum credible accident" was then described — the worst accident believed possible should all safety devices function as expected. In all cases the "maximum" accident was described as being quite minor — resulting in little or no melting of the reactor fuel, and little or no release of radioactivity to the outside air.

Recognizing, however, that neither human error nor mechanical failures were entirely predictable, and recognizing also that reactor behavior was not entirely understood, particularly under accident conditions, a second section of the hazards summary was devoted to "hypothetical accidents." In this section the applicant would describe his estimate of what the effects would be if, despite all foresight and planning, a serious accident within the reactor were to occur.

Such a hypothetical accident would be typically either a runaway caused by operator and mechanical error combined, or a "loss of coolant" accident, in which the cooling water would be lost or driven out of the reactor core. In such an accident, temperatures in the heart of the reactor would be expected to rise into the thousands of degrees within seconds, the uranium and steel of the fuel core would melt, and the melted metals would react chemically with the water still present.

Having made his estimate of the worst conceivable accident, the reactor builder would then go on to describe the measures he proposed to prevent its effects from reaching the public. Generally, this took the form of Beck's "thermos-bottle" — some sort of containment structure designed to withstand explosive pressure of a major accident. The Enrico Fermi Plant at Lagoona Beach, Michigan, was provided with a containment structure designed to withstand the explosive force of a thousand pounds of TNT. No matter what damage was done to the reactor, it was assumed that this containment would prevent any radioactivity from reaching the public.

Even in the days of small reactors, the "thermos-bottle" approach had many weaknesses. We have already seen that natural hazards, like earthquakes and landslides, often make nonsense of the containment idea, as the same agency which causes the accident is also likely to render useless the containment structures. In some reactor designs, like the popular boiling water reactor, numerous large pipes must pass in and out of the reactor through the containment structures. In addition, all reactor designs require a number of "penetrations" of the containment, including access ports for personnel, which make explosion-proof containment a more difficult task than it seems. Yet this approach had at least theoretical simplicity, and was little subject to mechanical or human failure.

The situation today is considerably more complicated. With modern large reactors, no feasible containment structure would serve unassisted, and a host of new devices are introduced. Applications for construction permits still have the same general form, although the "hazards analysis" has now been transmuted into a "safety analysis." The two general types of accidents are still described, but discussions of the "hypothetical" accident — a loss of coolant followed by melting of the reactor fuel — are considerably more elaborate.

One recent application, for instance, describes the worst accident case, in which all safety devices fail. The applicants do not consider this to be a credible occurrence. The only comment is a laconic: "The curve shows that the system pressure rises monotonically since there is no energy rejected from the system." [16] What this means in plain English is that the pressure goes on rising indefinitely until it bursts the containment structures and releases the radioactivity of the melted fuel to the outside air.

A number of elaborate devices are described which are intended to prevent such an event. There are two spray systems for cooling the reactor fuel, and two spray systems for cooling the containment itself. These are provided with an elaborate series of interlocking valves and sensing devices, so that a malfunction in them will not itself produce an accident. In the boiling water reactors, isolation valves and other devices are needed to prevent the accident pressures from blowing out the steam lines which run directly from the reactor core out of the containment and several hundred feet to a neighboring building where the turbines are housed.

An additional complication is provided by the fact that after the fuel melts, it reacts violently with whatever water is still present in the reactor vessel. The added heat and pressure from this reaction puts more strain on the containment. The reaction of uranium or zirconium (a common fuel-container material) with water releases hydrogen. If there is air present in the system, this hydrogen can explode. Much of the damage in the Chalk River accident was caused by such a hydrogen explosion, which lifted a 4-ton structure several feet in the air. In its application for a reactor to be built at Rock Island, Illinois, on the Mississippi, the Commonwealth Edison Company notes, ". . . the capability of the containment to withstand the burning hydrogen resulting from a metal-water reaction is limited. . . ." [17]

This is again a mild way of saying that a hydrogen explosion would burst the containment and release clouds of poisonous radioactivity. In order to prevent this from happening, elaborate precautions must be taken to keep any air from entering the primary containment system.

All of these safety devices must have their own safety devices to keep *them* from failing, and the whole complex of devices must be maintained in a state of readiness, so additional devices for *testing* the safety devices must be provided. All these devices, of course, work on electric power, which would not be available from the nuclear plant itself in the case of an accident, so power must be provided from outside, and in the case of outside power failure with supplementary emergency power. This latter is important, for because of the dependence of so many of the safety devices on outside power, a power failure might itself be the cause of an accident or associated with one. But emergency power, generally provided by a diesel-fueled generator, must be available within seconds because of the speed with which accidents occur in reactors, and therefore new problems are introduced in the effort to provide such a rapid changeover.

Each of these proliferating safety devices seems to introduce new problems of its own. For instance, the AEC's Advisory Committee on Reactor Safeguards recently pointed out that the shock of emergency cooling water in an accident might crack the heavy steel of the reactor vessel and create the very breach it was to prevent.[18]

As the hazards grow, the search for preventive measures tends to produce more and more exotic techniques. The Atomic Electric Power Company announced in July of 1967 their plans to build the two largest reactors yet — 1,100,000 kilowatts each — on the western shore of Lake Michigan. For these behemoths, Westinghouse proposes to enclose the entire containment system in a refrigerated ice pack; in case of accident, insulating panels would lift and the ice would cool off the reactor before it exploded.

These elaborate and exotic safety measures are attached to

reactors which are themselves untried and in many ways badly understood. The new huge reactors expose their fuels and structural materials to high temperatures and high intensities of radiation for longer periods of time than any power plants with which we have experience. Novel effects are constantly appearing. As the reactor program progressed, for instance, it was discovered that exposure to neutron radiation in a reactor core slowly makes steel brittle. More recently it has been discovered that this effect occurs in all metals, and is due at least in part to the formation of microscopic helium bubbles within the metal. No solution for this problem has yet been found, although several proposals have been made.

Another source of damage to steel is "hydrogen embrittlement"; radiation also has more direct, long-term effects on the strength and brittleness of steel, with at least the possibility that the reactor vessel itself could fail under the pressures generated by a loss of coolant or other severe accident. All of these potential accident hazards are failures which appear only after months or years of reactor operation. The new effects which will appear after a number of large reactors have been operating for years cannot even be guessed at.

All of these problems are aggravated by the high temperatures and pressures at which coming reactors will operate. The two reactors ordered by TVA for operation at Brown's Ferry, Alabama, 1,000,000-kilowatt plants produced by General Electric, will operate at a fuel temperature of 4200°F. This is close to the melting point of the uranium oxide fuel (about 5000°F); if the reactor exceeds its normal maximum power output by as little as 20 percent, the fuel will melt.

Stepping so close to the limits of safety has brought forth expressions of concern from many quarters. In a letter to the

Chairman of the Atomic Energy Commission, the Advisory Committee on Reactor Safeguards, although provisionally approving the application for the two Brown's Ferry plants, expressed a long list of reservations. It noted that in an accident, even if all emergency systems functioned adequately, "the calculated number of fuel elements reaching undesirably high temperatures is greater" than in smaller reactors. "Also, the time margin available for actuation of [emergency] systems is less."

"In a loss-of-coolant accident," the Committee notes, "the core spray systems are required to function effectively under circumstances in which some areas of fuel clad may have attained temperatures considerably higher than the maximum at which such sprays have been tested experimentally to date."

Operation with a fuel assembly slightly out of line could also cause local melting and perhaps worse accidents, the Committee noted. "The diesel-generator sets for emergency power appear to be fully loaded with little or no margin. . . . They are required to start, synchronize and carry load within less than thirty seconds. . . .

"The Committee wishes to emphasize the importance of quality assurance in fabrication . . . and of inspection. . . . Because of the higher power level and advanced thermal conditions in the Brown's Ferry Units, these matters assume even greater importance. . . . because the Brown's Ferry Units are to operate at substantially higher power level and power density than those on which . . . experience will be obtained, an especially extensive and careful start-up program will be required." [19]

Despite its multitude of reservations, the Committee recommended approval of the application, in part because of the "favorable characteristics of the proposed site," apparently a reference to the small number of people in the area. But in a completely unprecedented move, one member of the Committee declined to go along with the recommendation:

"It is my belief that the substantial increase in power and power density of the Brown's Ferry reactors over boiling water reactors previously approved should be accompanied by increased safeguard margins for the unexpected." The lone dissenter, Dr. Stephen Hanauer, went on to repeat some of the things which had disturbed the full Committee, adding, "The dependence on immediate availability of a large amount of emergency electrical power, using diesel generators operating fully loaded in a previously untried starting mode, is of special concern, as are the high temperatures and numerous fuel-element failures predicted even for successful operation of the emergency core cooling system in a large loss-of-coolant accident." [20]

These concerns about the reliability or effectiveness of emergency systems are particularly disturbing since publication of a report from the AEC's Advisory Task Force on Power Reactor Emergency Cooling. This report, which is undated but appeared late in 1967, considered the events which might follow the accidental interruption of normal cooling in "large, light-water power reactors as currently designed and located." As we have seen, any interruption in the flow of cooling water to an operating reactor would be quickly followed by melting of the fuel; elaborate devices have been planned to see that this is not followed in turn by a release of radioactivity from the molten fuel to the outside air. Containment vessels and emergency cooling devices serve this function.

What the Task Force report does is to state finally and clearly what had for some time been widely understood — that should

fuel melting occur in a large reactor, there is no assurance that
any device could prevent the release of massive amounts of
radioactivity to the outside air. Unless emergency measures in
the first seconds following an interruption of coolant flow manage to *prevent* melting, the result would be catastrophic.

> It was concluded that the description of the events that could
> take place subsequent to a postulated meltdown of large por-
> tions of a [fuel] core is at present indeterminate and quite spec-
> ulative. . . . Reliable and practical methods of containing the
> large molten masses of fuel that would probably result from such
> a meltdown do not exist today. . . . Accordingly, it is not con-
> sidered possible to assure the integrity of the containment if melt-
> down of large portions of the core were to occur.[21]

The report concludes that emergency cooling methods must
be available to prevent melting. Should the accident which
leads to loss of ordinary coolant flow also cause some disruption of the reactor fuel core arrangement, emergency cooling
systems might not work. Should the accident in some other
way disrupt the effectiveness of the emergency cooling system,
the fuel would melt, and once melted, would simply dissolve
any material in its way. Containment would be impossible.
(This has long been known in the reactor industry as the
"China problem": once collected in one place, molten fuel
would simply dissolve its way "clear down to China.") The
AEC must have had a pretty good idea of what the conclusions
of the report would be, for, late in 1966, it began putting pressure on the owners of already operating reactors to add emergency "core cooling" systems to the plants, a procedure which
in some cases may run into millions of dollars.

It is probably the conclusions of this report, long known in
advance or arrived at independently by others, which cause the

trepidation over uncertain, over-elaborate and possibly unreliable emergency devices expressed by Dr. Hanauer and others.

Despite such scattered warnings of coming trouble, the Price-Anderson Act shifts the burden of concern to the AEC, and utilities are pressing forward. In June 1967 a news report stated, "For the 1976 nuclear plant that it wants, Con Ed is studying the possibility of an underground installation in New York City." [22] On June 20, the Administrative Vice President of Consolidated Edison, W. Donham Crawford, announced the opening of a public-relations campaign to gain public acceptance of this project. Speaking to the Health Physics Society at its meeting in Washington, D.C., Crawford said,

> With a construction permit issued by 1972, an operating nuclear plant at an in-city site should be feasible by 1976.
>
> . . . Movies, slide presentations, pamphlets and even comic books have been utilized to convey the message that the atom is here to stay. . . . The utility companies can be expected to step up their efforts to inform the public of the need to locate nuclear stations within cities. Indeed, the remarks which I am now making may be construed as part of such an effort. [23]

Although the Atomic Energy Commission has repeatedly stated that they are not yet quite ready to approve plans like Con Ed's for reactors in the heart of a major city, nevertheless nuclear plants are being planned for heavily populated areas. The New Jersey Public Service Gas and Light Company proposed a plant, the size of the Brown's Ferry reactors, to be built in Burlington, New Jersey, less than five miles from the outskirts of Philadelphia. More than five million people would have lived within 25 miles of the plant. Almost the entire city of Burlington was within one and a half miles of the proposed plant site. The application has been withdrawn, although apparently only temporarily, in the face of probable AEC refusal.

Consolidated Edison has already announced plans for a third huge nuclear plant at its Indian Point site just 25 miles north of New York City; the two giant nuclear power and desalting plants proposed for Bolsa Island are less than a mile from densely populated Orange County and 24 miles from the center of Los Angeles. Yet, in April of 1967, a representative of the AEC's Advisory Committee on Reactor Safeguards testified before the Joint Committee on Atomic Energy that "the ACRS believes that placing large nuclear reactors close to population centers will require considerabe further improvements in safety, and that none of the large power reactors now under construction are considered suitable for location in metropolitan areas." [24]

In commenting on the AEC's position, the Washington editor of the trade journal *Nucleonics* notes that rural sites, even though there may be people living quite close to the reactor, are preferable to city sites. "Rural sites have three big things going: the ability of the atmosphere to disperse any accidental release is a 'God-given engineered safeguard,' a few people could be evacuated easier than a city's inhabitants, and the fewer people living in the area means there are fewer people to intervene in public hearings." [25]

This cynical portrayal of present reactor-siting policies may not comfort rural neighbors of nuclear plants. A news story in another trade publication on June 15, 1967, was headlined "How Connecticut Yankee Met a Public Acceptance Crisis"; it described efforts of the Connecticut Yankee Light and Power Company to circumvent public opposition to its reactor, which has now gone into operation near the small town of Haddam

Neck.[26] Several local residents, and the First Selectman of the town's Board, Charles J. Wolf, had written to the AEC asking for a public hearing on Connecticut Yankee's request for an operating license. According to the report, "Connecticut Yankee sent an executive to talk with Wolf, who subsequently withdrew his application for a hearing. . . ." The story also quotes the editor of a nearby newspaper: "Not everyone is happy with the idea of the plant being there, but they're pretty well resigned to it."

As the reactor program gathers momentum, and as the investment in it by utilities both public and private, by manufacturers, suppliers, and mining companies grows into the billions, it becomes more and more difficult to consider calmly the wisdom of the way in which the program is being pursued. WASH-740's ominous warning of thousands killed and billions of dollars in property damage is submerged under mountains of comic books featuring Citizen Atom and Reddy Kilowatt. Public relations is substituted for debate.

The difficulty, of course, is that the federal agencies responsible for assuring safety in the reactor program are themselves the architects of that program, and in no position to give it an objective evaluation. Yet before the program proceeds any further such an evaluation must be made, if only because serious accidents are not the only, and perhaps not even the worst, risk which an expanded program will carry.

V

RADIATION DAMAGE

During the Second World War, a large area in the Tennessee mountains was acquired by the Manhattan Engineer District (the atom bomb project). This site, which became known as Oak Ridge, was chosen for its remoteness, as it was to house much of the experimentation of the project, and eventually a substantial portion of the facilities for production of bomb material. One of the world's first reactors was housed at Oak Ridge; the first plants for separation of bomb-grade uranium were established there.

From its earliest days Oak Ridge was posed with the difficulties of disposing of radioactive wastes. Operations of the reactor and uranium plants, and the wide range of experimentation carried on, all produced a bewildering variety of waste products, from contaminated clothing to the enormously radioactive reactor fuel wastes. Disposal of these wastes was an entirely new problem; the characteristics of many of the wastes were unknown, their danger to man was unknown, and their behavior, once released into the atmosphere or water supply, was unpredictable.

For the most dilute and presumably least dangerous wastes, simple discharge into air or water seemed reasonable, but caution was generally taken even then. Even when it seemed that the quantity of radiation being released was far too small to do any damage, careful watch was kept.

White Oak Creek, which flowed through the Oak Ridge area, was one logical place to dump the least harmful of the radioactive garbage produced. Liquid wastes would be diluted by the waters of the stream, which emptied into the Clinch River, which would further dilute them before reaching populated areas. In order to gain better control of the dilution process, however, White Oak Creek was dammed, to form a pond or lake of about 55 acres. Wastes were dumped into the lake, where they would be retained for about 30 days before trickling out into the creek. At its deepest point, behind the dam, White Oak Lake was 11 feet deep.

The lake quickly blended into its natural surroundings. Aquatic plants took root; migratory waterfowl began appearing, and fed on the good-sized fish which bred in the lake's quiet water. No one could have guessed from looking at it that the lake and all its living things were contaminated by man-made radioactivity.

Every chemical element of which the earth and its inhabitants are made now has at least one radioactive "twin" or isotope created by man. Natural elements are fixed and stable: the iron, copper, oxygen, carbon, hydrogen, helium, the more familiar elements — as well as the rare and unfamiliar ones, krypton, xenon, lanthanum, tellurium — of which all things are built do not change. The familiar stability of our world lies in the enormous stability of these elements.

The only exceptions to this rule are the few and rare naturally-occurring radioactive elements. The first of these to be discovered was radium; other radioactive elements, including uranium and radioactive potassium, have been identified. For unknown reasons, these elements were subject to a slow disintegration. A sort of fever of decay seemed to afflict these elements, which released heat and other radiations while slowly changing into other, lighter elements. It gradually became understood that the atoms of these elements were expelling part of their own substance in the form of particles and rays. This discharge would go on until each atom had unburdened itself and become a stable element; in the case of uranium, particles would be emitted until the atom had become stable lead.

A way of measuring this process was contrived, and gave us the term "half-life." This is a measurement of the rate at which a radioactive element is decaying. In a block of uranium, each atom is stable for a very long time. After perhaps millions of years of stable existence, it will emit a particle (an "alpha" particle, identical to the nucleus of a helium atom), lightening itself and achieving a new level of stability. Further emissions follow over long periods of time, until the atom finally achieves a completely stable weight in the form of lead.

At any given moment in time, there will be a few of the enormous numbers of atoms in the uranium block which are undergoing decay. The number of atoms emitting particles at any time determines how quickly the material will be completely changed into a block of another element. The term "half-life" describes this rate: a half-life is the period of time in which one-half of the atoms of any quantity of an element will decay into another element.

Uranium has a half-life of 4.5 billion years. This means that at any one time only a very few uranium atoms are undergoing decay, and that it takes four and a half billion years for half the atoms of a block of uranium to decay. In the uranium remaining at the end of this time, atoms are still decaying at the same rate, so it will be another 4.5 billion years before half of the remaining uranium decays; after nine billion years only a quarter of the original block will remain, and after an additional 4.5 billion years half of *that* uranium will have decayed, and so on.

These, of course, are enormously long periods of time. The half-life of uranium is roughly equal to the estimated age of the earth, which means that half of the uranium present at the earth's formation is still with us. The earth will probably not exist long enough for the greater portion of the uranium still present to disappear.

Since the "radioactivity" of radioactive elements is produced by decaying atoms, a slow rate of decay means little radioactivity. Elements which are changing more quickly, such as radium, which also occurs naturally, produce more radiation and consequently can do more harm. Yet because it decays so much more quickly, radium is a very scarce element indeed. As a result, the radiation to which mankind and other living things have been exposed from radioactive minerals in the earth's crust has been extremely mild.

Yet naturally stable elements can be made radioactive, and this process occurs to a slight extent in nature. Cosmic rays, high energy atomic particles which come from the sun or from distant space beyond our solar system, are continually crashing into the earth's atmosphere at tremendous speeds. When these particles strike the stable atoms of oxygen, nitrogen or rare gases in the atmosphere, their stability is destroyed, and either directly or indirectly, radioactive isotopes or twins of common elements are formed. Thus cosmic rays are constantly creating radioactive carbon (carbon 14) which is a chemical twin for natural carbon (carbon 12). But radioactive carbon is unstable, and decays, with the emission of radiation. The half-life of carbon 14 is more than 5,000 years; still a long time, but very much shorter than the billions of years in which the half-life of uranium is measured.

Man has discovered many means of duplicating the feat of cosmic rays, and in a variety of devices, including accelerators, reactors and atomic bombs, has succeeded in creating at least one radioactive twin for every natural element. Some of these are so unstable that they vanish in a fraction of a second; others are stable enough to remain with us for thousands or millions of years. By far the greatest volume of these radioactive elements are made in reactors; they are the fragments of the split uranium atom or the unstable forms produced by the intense radiation of the uranium chain reaction. A single 1,000,-000-kilowatt reactor installation, after a year of operation, contains more radioactive strontium, cesium and iodine than was released in all the nuclear weapons tests conducted in the world until the present.[1]

The result of this ingenuity in disrupting the stability of atoms is that all living things, including man, are now exposed to a new source of radiation, potentially many times greater than the background of radiation from earth and sky to which life has gradually accustomed itself over the billions of years of its evolution. Each of us now carries some radioactive strontium in our bones, and some radioactive cesium in our muscles, and some radioactive carbon through all our body tissues, as a result of nuclear weapons testing. As we shall see, the significance of this fact is still obscure. How much damage will this radioactivity do? When bombs were first tested, we simply did not know. Although we are learning more about the problem, we still do not know the full answer.

It is true that all living things have adapted themselves to natural radiation — the cosmic rays from outer space, the radiation from rocks, and the radioactive materials which, in small quantities, are absorbed from the normal food we eat and use in the body. Evolution itself has probably been profoundly influenced by the mutations produced by such radiations. But what can happen to a species through eons of time is something different from rashly increasing artificial radiation in the course of a few years, with our imperfect knowledge of the harm that may be done.[2]

These words were written by Ritchie Calder in 1962, in *Living with the Atom,* a far from pessimistic examination of the peaceful uses of atomic energy. He was expressing a difficulty recognized by both proponents and critics of nuclear programs, a difficulty which stems from the large lead which our understanding of physics has over the science of biology. Although we have developed great ingenuity in creating radiation, we know very little about the way in which radiation affects living things; we know less about the ways in which radioactive or other pollutants affect the complex community of living things on which people depend.

White Oak Lake is, or was, a good illustration of what we do and don't know about the biological effects of radiation. Radioactive wastes discharged into the lake followed a very complex career. Radioactive cesium, for instance, is chemically identical to stable cesium, a rare element which is quite similar to potassium. Living things make little distinction between potassium, which is quite common, and cesium; potassium is particularly important to higher animals in nerve and muscle function. It is a vital constituent of every living cell.

The radioactive forms of cesium are formed in the splitting of uranium atoms. Since cesium is almost exactly half the weight of uranium, it is a common product of fission, and hence one of the principal forms of reactor waste. The half-life of the most common form of radiocesium, cesium 137, is a little more than 30 years.

If a tiny quantity of cesium is released into White Oak Lake, it does not simply disappear. It remains dissolved in the water of the lake for a time. In this form it may be absorbed by one of the microscopic plants which exist in the billions in the lake water; one of these algae, mistaking the cesium 137 for potassium, may incorporate it into its tissues. But in doing so the cesium is concentrated. That is, the tiny plants filter a large volume of water to find the potassium they need, extracting and concentrating it in their tissues. If cesium as well as potassium is present, it too is concentrated by the algae.

Tiny plants in the lake form the food of slightly larger animals, the zooplankton; these in turn are eaten by crustaceans, which are eaten by small fish, which are eaten by larger fish. At each link in this "food chain," the cesium 137 is passed on. The algae have concentrated the originally dilute cesium; by eating a large number of algae, the zooplankton further concentrate it; tiny crustaceans eat large numbers of their smaller victims; fish eat many crustaceans. At each step, cesium is not merely passed on, it is concentrated.

This ability of living things to extract and concentrate extremely dilute substances is quite remarkable. In Par Pond, a small lake very much like White Oak Lake and used for the same purposes at another atomic energy installation, this phenomenon was studied. During several months in 1962, the concentration of radioactive cesium in the water was only 0.033 picocuries per gram (a picocurie is a very small quantity of radioactivity, equivalent to a millionth of a millionth of a gram of radium). But the flesh of bass caught in the pond contained, on the average, 35 picocuries — a thousandfold increase.[3]

For other radioactive substances, the concentration factor was even higher. The *average* concentration of radioactive zinc in the bones of bluegill was 8720 times that of the water in which they swam. The concentration of radioactive strontium had increased more than 2000 times in the bones of these same fish.[4]

A great deal has been learned about the way in which radioactive materials are concentrated by different animals, much of it through investigation of the problem of fallout from weapons testing. The testing of nuclear weapons, in fact, was probably the most massive (and unintentional) experiment in biology ever undertaken, and the results are just beginning to come in. It will be many years before we fully understand the effects of fallout; certainly they were not even guessed at when testing began. In *Living with the Atom,* Ritchie Calder quotes a statement attributed to Clement Attlee, British Prime Minister at the time the first atom bomb was dropped in Japan:

> Of course, at the time we knew nothing, I certainly knew absolutely nothing, about the consequences of dropping the bomb except that it was larger than an ordinary bomb. . . . We knew nothing whatever at that time about the genetic effects of an atomic explosion. I knew nothing about fallout and all the rest of what emerged after Hiroshima. As far as I know, President Truman and Winston Churchill knew nothing of these things either, nor did Sir John Anderson, who co-ordinated research for our side. Whether the scientists directly concerned knew, or guessed, I do not know. But if they did, then as far as I am aware, they said nothing of it to those who had to make the decision.[5]

Calder comments that "it is debatable whether those scientists who were party to the decision did, in fact, know about the biological risks." In *Science and Survival*, the eminent biologist Barry Commoner points out that this ignorance persisted through the early years of bomb testing, and that in fact our knowledge of the biological effects of fallout has still not caught up with our skill in nuclear physics.

Commoner points out that in 1953, "the AEC stated that the only possible hazard to humans from strontium-90 [from fallout] would arise from 'the ingestion of bone splinters which might be intermingled with muscle tissue during butchering and cutting of the meat.' No mention was made of the simple biological fact that the milk from such an animal would also contain strontium-90. By 1956 the AEC had acknowledged that milk represented the most important source of strontium-90 in human food." [6]

Little by little, more was learned about the ways in which plants and animals concentrate chemicals in their tissues. Strontium, which resembles calcium, was concentrated in bones and milk; radioactive iodine would be concentrated by cows grazing over large areas in which fallout had settled. The iodine 131 in their milk would be further and drastically concentrated in the thyroid gland of anyone drinking the milk. Children, with their large milk consumption, were particularly vulnerable; a group of children in a particularly heavy fallout area of Utah is presently being studied by the Public Health Service, and a number of thyroid abnormalities which may be due to fallout have been discovered.

Some years ago, it was discovered that Eskimos were absorbing far more fallout radioactivity than people living in temperate zones, even though the distribution of fallout was believed to be just the reverse, with more falling in the temperate zones than at either the poles or the equator. The answer to this puzzle lay in the enormous concentrating ability of the Arctic food chain. The first link in this chain is the tough, scrubby lichen, which has the unusual characteristic of deriving its mineral nourishment from the air instead of from the soil. Ordinarily, dust and soil particles settling on the lichen provided it with needed minerals; when radioactive fallout joined the dust and soil, the lichen absorbed it too. These plants were and are extremely efficient collectors of fallout. They are also one of the principal foods of the caribou, which graze on them particularly in the winter, when other vegetation is scarce. Caribou may graze over large areas, thus effectively collecting and concentrating all the fallout which has descended in those areas. But the caribou in turn are an important — and in some areas and seasons almost the exclusive — food of Eskimos. Thus it was that the residents of Anaktavuk Pass and elsewhere received and go on receiving, as fallout continues to drift down from the stratosphere, radiation exposures which are close to, and in some cases may exceed what are considered maximum permissible exposures (we shall have more to say about radiation standards such as these later).[7]

Radioactive wastes from reactors contain the same substances that are found in fallout, which is not surprising, since both derive from the same source — atomic fission. (The fallout from hydrogen [fusion] bombs is also principally from their uranium or plutonium "trigger.") When released into the environment, they follow paths as complex and unpredictable as those of fallout components.

At White Oak Lake, the food chain did not end with fish. Birds fed on the fish, and on one occasion it was found that enormously dilute radioactive phosphorus had followed the long trail from water to algae to fish to bird; radiophosphorus was appearing in high concentration (compared to the level in the lake water) in the flight muscles of waterfowl.

The reactors for plutonium production at Hanford, near the town of Richland, Washington, empty their cooling water into the Columbia River. The discharge contains some of the fission products from the reactor fuel, as well as normal impurities which have been rendered radioactive, although this highly radioactive waste material is in small quantities and highly diluted. But in the Columbia River, as everywhere that there are living things, chemicals either stable or radioactive are picked up from the water and concentrated. Radioactivity of the Columbia River plankton — microscopic plants and animals — averages two thousand times the radioactivity of the water. Caddis fly larvae achieve concentrations 350,000 times that of the water. One survey of bird life on the river showed that the birds which feed on river insects have a high concentration of radioactivity, which is mainly radiophosphorus; first the insect and then the birds have selectively concentrated this isotope, even though it is only a tiny fraction of the total radioactivity in the water. Duck-egg yolks have 40,000 times the radioactivity of the river water; adult swallows have a concentration factor of 75,000.

At White Oak Lake, many of the birds were migratory. It is not known when it was first suggested that these birds might be carrying some radioactivity off with them when they continued their migrations. Probably this had not yet occurred to anyone when the Tennessee Valley Authority was asked to do an ecological survey of the area (the eight years which elapsed between the establishment of Oak Ridge and the making of this survey gives some idea of the nearly total ignorance of biological effects under which the early years of the atomic energy program were conducted).

The TVA scientists discovered that the thousands of water-fowl which migrated through White Oak Lake each year were picking up substantial quantities of radioactivity. The largest element in this contamination was again radiophosphorus; this isotope has a relatively short half-life of 14 days, and by the time the ducks left the lake again, was probably no more serious a problem than the longer-lived isotopes. Some of these latter, of course, would be around for a very long time. The scientists initiated a program of banding the ducks in the hope of getting back reports from hunters who shot them.

The reports, once they began coming in, showed that the radioactive ducks were being killed anywhere from the provinces of Canada to the counties of Texas. According to one report, this "winged radioactivity worried the health authorities quite a lot." [8]

What was happening in White Oak Lake was that the highly dilute wastes dumped into the water were being reconcentrated and then neatly packaged and dispatched all over the continent. When we remember that some migratory birds which stop in the United States are on their way from the Arctic to the Antarctic, the potential scope of this distribution is truly impressive.

Nor are birds the only agents by which radiation may be carried in unexpected directions. An article in the AEC's publication *Nuclear Safety* comments,

From the beginning of the atomic industry, the use of basins or other restricted aquatic environments for the disposal of radioactive wastes has prompted concern with regard to the possible avenues of escape of these materials. . . . Singularly lacking in most of this effort is research on the role of biological agents in the dispersal of radioactive contamination.[9]

The same article quotes a Russian study of possible spread of contamination from basins holding radioactive waste by aquatic insects that emerge and fly away from the basin. The authors estimate that from a typical small basin in mid-Russia, 200 million insects emerge each year (apparently caddis flies, mayflies and midges). Of these, 180 million would be eaten by predators — other insects and birds, which would presumably carry the contamination still further. The remaining 20 million insects would die and presumably be deposited in an area of radius 1.5 kilometers from the basin. The authors estimate that in this area the insect "fallout" would deposit as much radioactivity as the fallout from two hydrogen bomb tests (this refers to "stratospheric fallout" apparently, from far distant tests). The authors were pleased with these results, which indicated to them that insects could effect "a comparatively rapid and complete bioecological self-purification" of the waste basin.

Apparently no study of insect dispersal was done at White Oak Lake, nor is there any easy way of applying the Russians' figures. According to the article just quoted, "An almost complete lack of information on the numbers of individuals and population dynamics of aquatic insects makes it difficult to assess the applicability of these assumptions to other areas." But apparently the experience with the banded ducks was sufficient, for shortly after the results were in, White Oak Lake was drained.

There is literally no way of knowing what has happened to most of the radioactive chemicals which were dumped into White Oak Lake before it was drained. A given atom of radioactive cesium 137 may have passed from water to plankton to fish to bird, been transported thousands of miles; the bird may have been shot and eaten. This would not be the end of the cesium 137's career. After being retained in the muscle tissue of the man who had eaten the duck, perhaps for days or weeks, the cesium 137 atom would be excreted, picked up once again by plankton in a river, and perhaps pass again through fish, bird and man. Endless other paths might be followed. From White Oak Lake it might have been carried by an insect for a mile, and then with the death of the insect become part of the soil organic material which would cycle through plants and back to the soil for years or decades, until perhaps being ingested by another insect as part of a plant leaf and carried elsewhere, picked up by a bird and finally appearing in the human food supply a generation after its creation. Much of the lake water radioactivity may have passed to the sea before entering the biological community.

The half-life of cesium is about thirty years; even after ten half-lives, or three centuries, a fraction of any given amount of cesium will still remain. The half-life of strontium 90 is almost as long. The half-life of man-made plutonium is 24,000 years. The half-life of iodine 129, produced in small quantities in reactors, is 17,250,000 years.

All this means that every time radioactive waste is dumped into a stream, buried, dropped into the ocean, discharged into the air, or otherwise released from human control, it passes into the complex world of living things. It will pass from living thing to living thing, sometimes becoming concentrated, at other times being dispersed, with an efficiency and ingenuity which man has not yet come to understand. At unpredictable times and places, this radioactive waste will reappear in man's food, air or water. It will not go away, for decades or centuries or even millennia.

There is nothing new in this phenomenon. Nearly every

living animal on the surface of the globe, from deep-sea fish to Arctic birds, carries some DDT in its fatty tissues; the number of pesticides which are achieving such universality grows every year. Lead from gasoline additives can be found in the snows of the High Sierra. Nearly every child born on earth in the last ten years has carried some radioactive strontium in his bones. The amount of radioactive carbon in the atmosphere has been doubled, and all of us bear some of this burden in our tissues.

We are slowly coming to a realization that the thin film of life which covers the earth is a single complex web, and a chord plucked anywhere sends its vibrations worldwide. And man is a part of this web; he depends on it totally for his food, air and water.

What are the effects of radiation on man? Our ignorance of this subject is even greater than that of the means by which radiation returns to man's hand after being released into the environment.

Effects of radiation are divided into two classes by most scientists — somatic effects and genetic effects. The first refers to the effects of radiation on an exposed person's body (soma); the other refers to the effects on his progeny. Both kinds of effects are believed to be due to the same causes — the disruption by radiation of a cell's basic self-regulatory machinery. Whether this disruption eventually results in disease or in inherited malformation seems to depend simply on which of the body's cells is affected. Radiation lodged in a child's thyroid gland may produce cancer; radiation directed at the adult's gonads may, through a similar effect on germ tissue, produce mutation and malformation in later generations.

As we have seen, radioactive substances are chemically

identical to the familiar elements, except that they have been rendered unstable. In the process of changing, or decaying, from one form to another, they emit radiation. This radiation can be in the form of tiny particles, actually fragments of the atom, or as penetrating rays similar to X-rays. This radiation may pass through seemingly solid substances. Some particles, such as the heavy and slow-moving alpha rays, can penetrate only a thin sheet of paper; lighter beta rays may pass through several inches of wood or flesh; some penetrating gamma rays may pass through several feet of concrete.

When one of these particles or rays goes crashing through some material, it collides violently with atoms or molecules along the way. Such collisions are violent enough to tear away some of the electrons which form a cloud around every atom. Stripped of some of its electrons, the atom becomes a positively charged particle, or ion. Such a particle quickly undergoes violent chemical reactions with surrounding molecules as it returns to a neutral state.

Radioactive substances in food are incorporated into tissue just as their stable twins would be; imbedded deep within a cell, the radioactive atom may emit a particle which then streaks away, leaving a track of ions in its path. These ions then undergo sudden and violent chemical combination with surrounding molecules. In the delicately balanced economy of the cell, this sudden disruption can be disastrous. The individual cell may die; it may recover. But if it does recover, its self-regulatory powers may be affected in some way we do not yet understand. After the passage of weeks, months or years, it may begin to proliferate wildly in the uncontrolled growth we call cancer.

It hardly needs to be pointed out that we do not know exactly how cancers are caused; we do not know exactly what changes induced by ionizing radiation cause the cell to become cancerous. This is simply part of our greater ignorance of basic life processes, for although newspaper headlines have given the contrary impression in recent years, biologists are not at all in agreement about what makes living things tick.

For a time, following important discoveries made in the 1950's, it was believed that a single chemical, DNA (deoxyribonucleic acid), was the "master chemical" of the cell. This enormously complex molecule, which is found mainly in the cell's chromosomes, was believed to direct the activities of the living thing very much the way a punched paper tape regulates some automatic machines. Different chemical groups strung along the molecule were believed to act like the holes in a paper tape which, slowly unreeling, directed the growth, differentiation and lifelong activities of all living things; DNA was also believed able to duplicate itself and therefore embodied in itself all the characteristics of life.

While this theory held sway, it was tempting to explain the damage done by radiation in terms of DNA; if a particle smashed into one of the key DNA molecules, part of the "instructions" coded into the molecule would be obliterated. If a sufficient number of instructions were erased, the cell would simply cease to function. Smaller alterations in the DNA would produce abnormal functioning, perhaps including cancer development.[10] Since it was the DNA which was responsible for duplication and inheritance, any alterations in DNA would pass on from generation to generation — providing a simple explanation of the phenomenon of mutation.

Despite the early enthusiasm with which the theory of DNA as the "secret of life" was received by biologists, experimental evidence gathered in recent years is beginning to suggest that it is far too simple. This evidence is summarized in very readable form in *Science and Survival,* a book by the biologist Barry Commoner, himself the leading critic of what is half humorously referred to by its proponents as the "dogma" of DNA.

What the new evidence seems to suggest is that the living cell is a complex whole of which DNA is only a dependent — although important — part.

According to the newer view, self-duplication and other life processes can only be carried out by a properly functioning intact cell; damage to the DNA by radiation or other causes may result in imperfect duplication, and hence inherited defects — but damage to other parts of the cell's complex machinery may also cause such mutations.

Because the cell is a complex of interdependent processes, disturbance of one process may resonate through the whole system, causing a chain of tiny disturbances in the cell which our knowledge is simply not yet adequate to trace. On a microscopic scale, the release of radiation within the cell is very much like the release of radiation into the macroscopic human environment. Once the complex living system is disturbed, we are at a loss to predict the ultimate consequences. Under what circumstances the disturbance of a cell may result years later in the formation of a cancerous growth, we simply do not know; we are equally ignorant of the circumstances under which a cell may recover from radiation damage, or, in most cases, of those in which a mutation is induced.

Still more mysterious is another effect of radiation on most living things — life-shortening. Exposed to low doses of radiation over long periods of time, a wide range of animals and insects show no visible damage, except that their lives become shorter. Radiation has somehow accelerated the aging process. This effect is believed to occur also in man. Very little is known about how radiation shortens lives, but it is generally held that it does so by speeding up the normal process of aging. Unfortunately, once again our knowledge of biology is inadequate; Dr. Herman Blumenthal writes: "The problem of life-shortening effects [of radiation] has received only brief consideration. . . ." [11]

Dr. Blumenthal describes one likely explanation of the life-shortening effect. As a person grows older, more and more of the cells of his body show definite alterations, or mutations. These may be caused by natural radiation, or other factors. If the disturbance to a given cell is not lethal, it may cause significant alterations in the cell's proteins.

> The consequences of these alterations involve the concept of biological individuality which holds that, except in the case of identical twins, each individual's proteins differ in some subtle way from those of every other individual. The rejection of organs transplanted from one person to another, which has received so much attention in recent years, is based on this principle. The transplanted organ, which has a different "individuality" from that of the recipient, gives rise to an immune reaction from its host, and the result is its rejection. The analogy in respect to aging would be that mutations occurring in a particular organ would render the mutated cells of the organ "foreign" and thus lead to an autoimmune reaction. [12]

The process of aging is therefore seen as the body's attack on its own tissues, as these are subtly altered over the years. Since radiation is known to produce mutations in all cells, it is reasonable that constant low levels of radiation exposure simply hasten the process of change which leads to aging.

Dr. Blumenthal points out that there is gathering evidence that this attack of the body in its own tissues may be involved in a number of the diseases of the old, as well as in aging itself. He includes vascular disease, cancer, diabetes, "and several of the less frequent diseases of old people." There is a suggestion, therefore, that all of the effects of radiation — cancer, inherited malformation, and life-shortening — may all be due to the same cause, a subtle reorganization of the body's cells following a damage from radiation.

Single living things are complicated systems, no less than the communities of living things in which they may be placed. A single nuclear particle smashes into a cell; the cell, itself a highly complex assortment of interdependent processes, undergoes complex alterations to adjust itself to the damage. The changed cell, if it is a germ cell, will eventually result in offspring which are different from the parent. If it is a body cell, its alteration may set off complex responses in the larger organism which, years later, may result in cancer or other disease. Repeated damage to cells may set off the complex degenerative process of senescence.

All of what we have said gives some picture of the difficulties of estimating the damage to people from a given amount of radiation in the environment. Let us take, for instance, the problem of estimating the number of human mutations which would be induced by dumping a given amount of radioactive cesium into White Oak Lake.

This small quantity of cesium 137 may be concentrated in the food chain of the lake; it may be further dispersed by insects; it may be carried away by birds which upon dying in remote areas decompose and further disperse the radioactivity; it may be carried to the sea or enter the groundwater. Should it be concentrated in the muscles of a waterfowl, that bird might be shot by a hunter and then eaten. The cesium 137 would then be concentrated in the hunter's muscles; some of its radiation might reach his germ tissues. A single particle might crash through a germ cell, damaging without killing it; the damaged cell might, years later, produce a damaged sperm which might fertilize an egg and result in the birth of a child with some defect.

The cesium 137, whose half-life is roughly thirty years, would soon be excreted from the hunter's body, whether or not it had done any damage there, and continue its complex career through the world of living things for decades or centuries, at each passage through the human food chain creating a new risk of damage.

What then is the risk of genetic damage from a given amount of cesium 137 released into the environment? We can only say that with *any* release of radioactivity there is *some* risk of damage. This risk grows steadily with every release of radioactive waste anywhere in the world, and the risk is shared by all of us.

As the nuclear reactor program expands, its wastes will also increase, and the burden of radioactivity in our surroundings will rise, and go on rising. At some point the deleterious effects of this radiation will become unacceptable even to a nation which is able to tolerate 50,000 deaths on its roads each year. Because the effects of radiation go on making themselves felt decades after the first damage is done, it would be well to anticipate the eventual saturation of our surroundings. For the environment which supports us has only a limited capacity for radiation, and that capacity can only be used once.

VI

A NEW POLLUTION PROBLEM

In August of 1963, the Pacific Gas and Electric Company started up its reactor at Humboldt Bay on the Northern California coast. Late in the same year, General Electric, manufacturer of the reactor, began discovering difficulties in its design. These began showing up at the elaborate testing and research facilities GE maintained at Vallecitos, near Pleasanton, California. The stainless-steel encased fuel rods for the reactors were showing signs of cracking during reactor operation.

Uranium fuel for a reactor, as we have said, is compressed into pellets and loaded into long thin rods, about half an inch thick and several feet long. The rods are bundled together into "fuel assemblies" for ease of handling. The material from which to make the fuel tubes, or "cladding," posed an early problem for the reactor industry, which has not yet been entirely solved. This material must be thin, and yet capable of withstanding temperatures of several hundred degrees, and high pressures, for a year or more of reactor operation, while all the time being exposed to intense radiation which causes degenerative effects in most materials.

The search for a suitable fuel container led to some fairly exotic materials. An alloy called zircaloy was developed and used in the nuclear submarine program — the submarines are powered by reactors which served as the early prototypes for some present commercial power reactors.

General Electric, trying to bring the price of its reactors down, settled on stainless steel for its fuel cladding, and the Humboldt reactor was equipped with a fuel core of uranium oxide in stainless steel jackets. By late 1963, it was becoming clear that the choice of stainless steel for the Humboldt reactor was a mistake. Test fuels at Vallecitos were cracking and flaking — but the initial fuel loading for Humboldt, worth about four million dollars, had already been made, and the reactor went into operation on schedule. At that point Pacific Gas and Electric knew it would eventually run into trouble. Arrangements were made to replace the stainless steel with zircaloy-clad fuel, which seemed more reliable. But the replacement was not to be made until the first loading of stainless steel fuel had been used.

By June of 1965, the expected problems began to materialize. The radioactivity being discharged from the plant's stack began slowly to increase. In the reactor's core, the long slender fuel rods were beginning to show cracks and tiny leaks. Radioactive wastes from the fission process going on in the uranium within the rods were leaking out through the stainless steel containers and into the cooling water flowing between the rods. Some of these radioactive wastes were gases and, mingling with the steam produced in the reactor, were piped out to the turbines which drove the power generators. Passing through the turbines, both gases and steam were passed into a condenser cooled with sea water; here the steam was cooled back to water and returned to the reactor, but the radioactive gases were separated and discharged through the plant's tall stack. (This is a common and routine waste disposal procedure.)

In order to slow down the disintegration of the stainless steel fuel, P. G. & E. was operating the reactor at only a fraction of its full power. Nevertheless, radioactive discharges continued to increase, and by September, 1965, the release rate had climbed to 85,000 microcuries per second,[1] although the maximum average annual release permitted by the AEC was 50,000 microcuries per second. Testifying somewhat later before a California State Assembly Committee, P. G. & E. denied that release rates exceeded AEC limits, and pointed out that "AEC and State regulations limit these emissions to 50,000 microcuries per second on an *annual average basis* [emphasis in the original]; yet, during all of 1965 the emissions reached an annual average of only 8,300 microcuries per second, or less than one-sixth the permissible amount." [2]

Despite these protestations, it seemed likely that increasing emissions, if continued, would eventually exceed permissible limits even on a "yearly average" basis. On September 14, 1965, P. G. & E. shut down the plant for refueling and modifications. The company denied that there was any connection between the shutdown and the increasing emissions: "The schedule for the outage [shutdown] was chosen to fit refueling requirements of the reactor," said the company's spokesman.[3] The plant was out of commission until early December; during this time about one-quarter of the stainless-steel fuel elements were removed and replaced with zirconium-clad fuel. Most or all of the badly leaking fuel rods, the company announced, had been removed.

Soon after start-up, however, radioactivity in the plant's stack gases started inching up again, and in the period February to August, 1966, it was reported to be ranging upward toward 40,000 microcuries per second, close to the permitted maximum.[4] On February 18, 1966, P. G. & E. applied to the AEC for a fourfold increase in allowed releases. In proposed Change No. 20, the company asked that their operating license be changed to allow emission of 210,000 microcuries of radioactive gases per second as an annual average, with ten times that amount for the maximum rate at any one time. The latter limit would have allowed a release of as much as 181,440 *curies* per day, for as long as a month, without exceeding permissible limits. This is a staggering quantity of radioactivity, equivalent to about 400 pounds of radium each day, or six tons of radium in a month.

It should be noted here that the radioactive gases under discussion are noble gases, principally radioactive xenon and krypton; these are relatively inactive chemically and are not incorporated to any great extent by living things. Thus, while breathing radioactive krypton exposes one to external and internal radiation, and small quantities would be dissolved in body fluids, essentially none would be incorporated into tissue. Radium, on the other hand, is readily incorporated into bone, where it remains for a long time, releasing radiation. Although the noble gases of one day's permissible release, according to P. G. & E.'s request, would be equivalent, in the radioactive energy it released, to 400 pounds of radium, the biological hazard would be far less than if the release were actually radium.

Other materials than noble gases are released from the reactor's smokestack, the principal one being radioactive iodine. Iodine 131 and other radioactive isotopes of iodine are biologically active, and are concentrated by the thyroid gland of people and animals. These isotopes therefore pose a far greater hazard than the noble gases; the requested level for iodine emission was 0.8 microcurie per second annually, with a maximum at any time of 8 microcuries per second. This could result in the release of 20,000,000 microcuries, or 20 curies, during a single month without exceeding the limit; considering the potency of radioiodine, this is still a very substantial amount.

P. G. & E. did not base its request for an increase in emission rates on the difficulty it was having with its fuel, nor on the slowly rising levels of radioactivity coming from the plant. In September of 1966, P. G. & E. public relations man Hal Stroube submitted testimony to a State Assembly committee that:

> P. G. & E.'s application for the "fourfold increase" in the permissible stack release rate . . . resulted from a commitment made by P. G. & E. to the AEC in 1962. At that time the company agreed to perform a detailed meteorological study in the plant's environs to establish the correct stack release limit. . . . The meteorological study was completed in late 1965 and formed the basis for the application. There was no direct connection between the application and the alleged "alarming rise in the level of radioactive gas." [5]

Despite this protestation, however, the application itself, signed by S. L. Sibley, company president, stated, "Authorization is requested by May 1966 because operation of the unit is expected to be affected by the present limits within a few months." [6]

The P. G. & E. application was denied by the AEC in August of 1966, and in the fall another two quarters of the steel-clad fuel was replaced by zirconium-clad elements. P. G. & E. hoped that the replacement of the fuel would allow it to operate the plant at full power; the reactor had been operating at only 40 percent of its rated capacity. Had it been operated at full capacity, the radioactive emissions would of course have been far larger, but according to Mr. Stroube, this was not the reason for operating at a lower power level. With surprising frankness he commented,

> The unit currently is being operated at 40 percent of its rated power (20,000 kilowatts of its original rating of 50,000 kilowatts) in order to extend the life of the remaining stainless steel-clad fuel in the core. This is in the interest of achieving maximum fuel economy and has no relation to public health and safety.[7]

Mr. Stroube did insist, however, that emissions at full power would not exceed AEC limits. These limits would allow an average of 50,000 microcuries to be released each second for a year. If the reactor operated at this level, it would release the staggering quantity of 1.5 million curies each year — the radioactive equivalent of a ton and a half of radium.

What relation does the release of such enormous quantities of radiation have to "public health and safety"?

The Atomic Energy Commission regulations are not designed to limit the total amount of radioactivity released into air or water by any plant. Instead, their regulations seek to insure that radioactivity, in whatever amount, is released in such a way as not to harm plant employees or the nearby public. Regulations for the amount of radioactive gas which can be emitted from a reactor state that they must be such that a person spending all his time at the plant's boundary will not receive more than a specified small exposure to radioactivity. In releasing gases, therefore, the reactor operators first dilute them with large volumes of air and then discharge them through a tall stack, so that by the time they reach the outside public they have been considerably dispersed and no one person can acquire an exposure beyond the limits set.

Because, as we saw in the last chapter, any exposure to radiation, no matter how slight, may produce some damage, the setting of limits is a difficult business. A complex philosophy and elaborate techniques have been developed since the end of World War II to deal with this problem. One long-standing principle has been that large numbers of people should never be exposed to more than the equivalent of the natural or "background" radiation to which they are always exposed. This is a necessarily arbitrary standard, and seems to stem at least in part from the idea that exposures below this level would produce some damage, but not enough to be easily distinguished from the bodily and genetic damage already being done by natural radiation.

It should be pointed out that the reassuring adjective "natural" does not imply that radiation from minerals and cosmic rays is harmless. On the contrary, it does the same sorts of damage and in the same ways as artificial radiation. Radioactive potassium in sea water is just as harmful as radioactive potassium made artificially. Radium and thorium which are naturally present in small quantities in coal are released into the air when coal is burned. Coal-burning power plants therefore release measurable quantities of radioactivity from their smokestacks and pose a small hazard of their own.

In other words, man-made radioactivity once released is simply an *increase* of a hazard already present. Those considering setting radiation standards generally seem to feel that a

new risk of about the same size as the old risk which has always
been around is acceptable. This is one approach to standard
setting, but there are clearly others.

The second widely accepted principle is that of balancing
benefits against risks. This is the approach which has been
taken by the Federal Radiation Council, a cabinet-level committee which advises the President on radiation standards.
The FRC's standards are not binding unless adopted by a governmental agency. The principal two federal agencies dealing
with atomic energy are the AEC and the Defense Department;
the AEC sets its own standards and regulations, many of which
predate the FRC (which was formed in 1959) — and the Defense Department apparently just ignores FRC standards.
According to one source,[8] Defense had insisted from the first
that they be exempted from any standards set outside the
Department, and finally extracted an explicit statement in an
FRC memorandum dated May 13, 1960, regarding radiation
"guides" established by the FRC. The memorandum said, "The
guides may be exceeded only after the Federal agency having
jurisdiction over the matter has carefully considered the reason
for doing so in the light of the recommendations of this paper."

Despite the fact that its recommendations were binding on
no one, the Federal Radiation Council issued a number of
standards or guides. These were at first called Radiation Protection Guides, or RPG's. Since at the time of their issuance
the principal source of radioactivity was fallout from nuclear
weapons testing, the RPG's were universally treated by the
press as safe limits below which fallout was harmless. Numerous reassuring statements, that exposures to fallout were only
a small fraction of those considered safe, were generally based
on these RPG's.

Treating the guides as safety standards was simply misleading, as they were nothing of the sort. We have already seen that there is no "safe" level of radiation exposure. What the Federal Radiation Council had done was to strike a balance between the benefits and risks, as they saw them, of the then principal source of radiation exposure, weapons testing. Rough estimates of the damage which would be done by fall-out in terms of increased numbers of thyroid cancers, cases of leukemia, mutations and other forms of damage were made, although not at first released. Benefits of weapons testing were presumably estimated in some fashion, although how this was done or could be done is unclear. A balance was then struck — the radiation protection guide represented the greatest exposure to radiation which the whole population might receive for which the benefits to the population outweighed the damage done.

This is a far cry from a safety standard, of course. Nor is it easy to see how any group, even a committee of cabinet officers, could carry out the procedure just described. For neither the benefits nor the risks of bomb testing could really be put into numbers easily, and even if they could be, the result would not necessarily be very useful. How many dollars saved in the weapons program, or how many new bombs, are justified by how many cases of leukemia?

What actually seems to have happened is that estimates of radiation damage were made from experiments on animals and past exposures of people to X-rays and radium in medical treatment. From these estimates, a guess was made of the amount of exposure of a large number of people which would clearly show damage to the population above and beyond that already being done by natural factors. Thus, estimates of leukemia or thyroid cancer production by artificial means were constantly compared, in FRC reports, with the natural incidence of these diseases.

When this exposure had been estimated, it was reduced by a substantial margin of safety, and then the reduced figure was issued as a "radiation protection guide." In short, despite the FRC trappings of balancing benefit against risk, they were following precisely the philosophy of the AEC in simply assuming that damage which could not be differentiated from natural causes was acceptable.

There are a number of other agencies which issue radiation standards. The International Commission for Radiation Protection, successor to the International Congress of Radiologists, is affiliated with the World Health Organization, and issued the first recommendations for limits of exposure to the general population from artificial radioactivity; these recommendations became the basis of many later standards. The National Committee on Radiation Protection and measurements is the successor to the United States radiologists' organization; this remains a private organization although it is closely associated with the Bureau of Standards of the U.S. Department of Commerce. Its recommendations have force only if adopted by government agencies.

The AEC has regulations for its own activities and those of its licensees; the Defense Department has its own regulations. Not all radiation is under the jurisdiction of the Federal Government: the states regulate uses of X-rays, radium, and, under agreements with the AEC, a number of other activities. The operations of uranium mines are under a number of overlapping federal, state and local jurisdictions, as are transportation of radioactive materials, waste disposal, and operation of atomic-powered ships, rockets and other devices.

There is a growing proliferation of agencies which in some way are responsible for regulating activities which do or might result in exposure of the general public to radiation. On the other hand, there is no agency with overall responsibility for finding out what total exposures to the population are and setting standards or limits. The result has been the almost universal adoption of the AEC's — and in present circumstances the only feasible — approach. This is simply to make sure that in every activity or device which exposes people to radiation, there is no release which would cause noticeable harm to the people directly exposed. Generally speaking, it seems safe to say that radiation exposures about equal to natural background will produce damage which is not noticeable, and emissions are kept to this level.

There is clearly a great deal wrong with the current state of affairs. First off, there is a world of difference between "no damage" and "no noticeable damage." Reactors, X-ray machines and even coal-burning plants are doing *some* damage; because so many people throughout the world ordinarily die from cancer, many thousands of additional cases could go by without notice. The fact that our biological knowledge or statistical techniques do not allow us to identify the small boy whose leukemia is a result of bomb testing does not mean that he does not exist.

The principle of keeping radiation exposures below the limit of noticeable damage is therefore perfectly arbitrary, and gains its appeal from the false reassurance derived from not actually seeing the damage being done. Whether in fact the benefits from reactors or other atomic energy devices justify

the damage being done is a question which remains un-
resolved as long as the damages do not obtrude themselves into
the public consciousness.

Secondly, the "no measurable damage" principle is based
on a simplistic and inaccurate picture of the living world.
It is possible to ignore the absolute quantity of radioactive
wastes being discharged into our air and water only when it
is assumed that, once sufficiently diluted, the wastes have
ceased to be a problem. In the last chapter we have seen that
this is emphatically not the case. Many of the radioactive
wastes produced by reactors are long-lived and biologically
active; iodine 129, which is selectively absorbed by the thyroid
gland, and hence poses a special threat through concentration
in that organ, has a half-life of more than 17 million years; although this isotope is produced in very small quantities by
reactors, the amount of iodine 129 in the environment must
steadily increase as the reactor program expands.

One of the radioactive gases being released by reactors poses
a similar and perhaps more immediate problem. A recently
published study estimates that radioactive krypton 85 will be
produced in such enormous quantities by the reactor program
that in less than a hundred years man's exposure to radiation
may be nearly doubled.[9] This is a profoundly disturbing prospect, for, of course, krypton 85 is only one of the many radioactive wastes to which we are to be exposed.

Another source of exposure which may someday become
serious is tritium, the radioactive form of hydrogen. Two or
three thousand curies of this material, which is almost impossible to separate from the water of which it becomes a part,
are discharged each year from each of the larger reactors
planned.

What will be the effect of increasing radiation exposure for all living things? We have very little idea. Our understanding of life is too primitive for us to know. The rate of mutation will certainly increase — and a beneficial mutation in man has never been recorded. Subtle effects are more likely to predominate than dramatic ones — slightly increased disease rates, slightly shortened life spans, subtle readjustments in the balance of species.

We can see that the present approach to radiation limits is inadequate, and sooner or later will lead to serious trouble. What we have been doing, quite simply, is to avoid killing or injuring anyone directly by spreading the damage thin over the whole environment. But that damage will not disappear, it will accumulate, slowly and inevitably, until the level of "no noticeable damage" is passed not for a single isolated area, but for the earth as a whole.

At present, saltwater fish caught far from land contain some DDT, washed from fields to streams and to the ocean, being concentrated by microscopic plants and animals, and then by the fish themselves. Nearly every bite of food each of us in this country takes adds another dose of pesticide to our bodies. Rainwater throughout the country contains a bewildering variety of chemicals, ranging from nitrates from agricultural fertilizer to gasoline additives.

Radioactive wastes are now beginning to repeat this pattern, and in the coming years our food and water will be increasingly burdened with radiation. The first step in this new assault on the environment was taken with atomic bomb testing, in secrecy and in almost complete ignorance. That first step having been taken, we are continuing with nuclear power plants. In other forms of air and water pollution, we had to reach the point of real disaster before beginning to think of control. This must not be allowed to happen with radioactive wastes; once released into the atmosphere, there is no conceivable way of retrieving radioactive gases; once entered on their winding course through the environment, radioactive isotopes are out of reach of man's control. The damage, once done, is irremediable. There is a real danger that such damage may be quite extensive before it is brought home to us, for the effects of radiation are so often far removed in time and place from their cause.

It is not only the nearby neighbors of reactors, therefore, who should be concerned with the radioactive poisons they release. Those releases are contributing to the slow degeneration of the environment in which we all live; radiation is the most serious of the many stresses we are putting on the fabric of life. Rachel Carson quotes in *Silent Spring* the ecologist Paul Shepard, who sees us stumbling toward a "life with only its head out of water, inches above the limits of toleration of the corruption of its own environment . . . Why should we tolerate a diet of weak poisons, a home in insipid surroundings, a circle of acquaintances who are not quite our enemies, the noise of motors with just enough relief to prevent insanity? Who would want to live in a world which is just not quite fatal?"

It is long past time that we realized that in radiation "no measurable damage" eventually means "just not quite fatal" for everyone. The haste with which the commercial reactor program is being pursued at present simply does not allow reasonable consideration of this problem. The Humboldt reactor is an excellent example of the kind of difficulty which is in store for us. The reactor was built, and its fuel core fabricated, before the difficulties of the fuel became apparent. This happened in 1963. By 1966, the reactor boom was on, and twenty power plants were ordered in that year; yet by mid-1967 a whole new series of fuel problems were beginning to appear.

There are only two types of fuel cladding tubes in widespread use in this country or planned for the near future — stainless steel and zirconium alloy (zircaloy). A hot debate rages in the industry as to the relative merits of the two fuel jackets, for both have suffered difficulties. (At present, zircaloy seems to have triumphed.) In hearings before the Joint Committee on Atomic Energy early in 1967, these problems were discussed, briefly. Congressman Craig Hosmer quizzed members of the AEC and its staff:

> Representative Hosmer: We had some cracks out at Dresden No. 1 in the zirc cladding to begin with.
>
> Mr. Shaw: In the boiling water reactor?
>
> Mr. Ramey: They took care of those.
>
> Representative Hosmer: They put stainless steel in, did they not? . . .
>
> Mr. Johnson: I think they started with zircaloy and changed over to stainless and then back to zircaloy later. That is my recollection.[10]

Hosmer was also interested in more recent fuel problems, particularly at the Big Rock Point reactor at Charlevoix, Michigan, and the Carolinas–Virginia Tube Reactor (CVTR) at Parr, South Carolina. The Big Rock Point plant, operated by the Consumers Power Company, had been suffering problems with its stainless steel clad fuel for over a year. The Consumers

Power Company reported that "the stainless steel seems to have been subjected to some sort of stress corrosion attack. . . ." The stainless steel fuel elements, like those at Humboldt, were being replaced by zircaloy-clad fuel; all the fuel was expected to be replaced by the end of 1967.

At Parr, South Carolina, however, the trouble was with zircaloy-clad fuel. The Carolinas–Virginia Tube Reactor is owned by four Southern utilities. In response to Representative Hosmer's question, Milton Shaw, Director of the AEC Division of Reactor Development and Technology testified:

> We had four test fuel samples in the reactor. Of these four development samples, three have failed long before achieving the design exposure levels.
>
> We are quite concerned about the implications of the failure of these fuel assemblies. As a result, we have gone ahead and removed the fourth assembly. . . .
>
> In addition, the CVTR has also experienced failures in two of the normal fuel assemblies clad with zircaloy 4 — the same material being planned for other commercial plants. . . .
>
> The first part of your question was related to the situation at the Consumers of Michigan Plant at Big Rock Point. This is a boiling water plant. They have been experiencing fuel cladding failures in both stainless steel and Incaloy bundles over a longer period of time. These failures, too, are being examined to determine the exact cause of the problem.
>
> Representative Hosmer: Is this the kind of fuel that is being sold commercially for other reactors, too?
>
> Mr. Shaw: Yes sir, stainless steel, zircaloy 4, and Incaloy 800 clad fuel has been sold for commercial reactors.

Representative Hosmer: How serious should we regard this, or can we make a judgment at this point?

Mr. Shaw: Although there is serious concern, I don't believe we can make a judgment at this time in the absence of determinations as to what caused the failures, sir. The failure could have been caused by defective manufacturing techniques or by something not understood about the design of the fuel.[11]

At the time Mr. Shaw was speaking, March 15, 1967, sixteen large new power reactors were under construction, and, by the first of July, orders had been placed for thirty-six more; utilities across the country had indicated plans for about two dozen further plants which had not yet been ordered. Seventy or eighty large reactors were being planned, then, or were already under construction, representing an investment of capital of several billion dollars. Roughly one-quarter of the initial investment in a reactor is its first batch of fuel; over the plant's life, the cost of fuel and fuel services is roughly equal to the initial cost of the plant itself.

In the face of this enormous investment, it is almost certain that presently available fuel tube materials will be used: the story of Humboldt Bay is about to be repeated on a massive scale. There, despite early signs of trouble with stainless steel, the first fuel loading was used and the reactor operated with some defective elements. At this writing, it is not known whether the difficulties with the three fuel cladding types reported by Mr. Shaw were due to faulty manufacture or "something not understood about the design of the fuel."

What is disturbing here is that there will be a number of reactors going into operation, as well as the dozen or so already in commercial use, which will necessarily rely on fuel which is presently available, not prohibitively expensive, but liable to failure and radioactivity release. Still more disturbing is the pattern which has been established and which will apparently continue. The rest of Mr. Shaw's testimony is illuminating:

> The general information available on water plant fuel, such as burnup and power densities, is sufficient that we know a safe and reliable fuel can be designed for the water reactor plants, if one doesn't extrapolate too far.
>
> However, there is no question but that the fuel warranties being provided right now [by manufacturers] far exceed the meaningful information which is available to us through the research and development programs.[12]

Translated, this means simply that we have now acquired enough information to design fuel for the plants which are presently in operation — that is, plants which were being built ten years ago. We do *not* have enough information yet to design safe and reliable fuel for the reactors now being built and planned, which are many times larger, and which expose their fuel to higher temperatures, higher radiation intensities and higher pressures for longer periods of time. The result will be operation of the plants with some faulty fuel elements for several years; but by then the industry hopes to have under construction the *next* generation of reactors (described in the next chapter) which have a whole new set of problems, many of them still more severe than those now being faced.

We seem to be permanently committed to a program, then, which is just a little bit ahead of the state of technology. This has been a long-standing state of affairs. In its 1962 report to the President, the Atomic Energy Commission stated:

Attempts to optimize economies by working on the outer fringes of technical experience, together with the difficulties always experienced in a new and rapidly advancing technology, have led to many disappointments and frustrations. . . . Such difficulties led to considerable diminution of the earlier optimism regarding the early utilization of nuclear power, which in turn contributed to the withdrawal of some equipment and component manufacturers from the field.[13]

The industry continues to work at the outer fringes of technical experience, as Mr. Shaw pointed out. In earlier chapters we considered the possible damages from a severe reactor accident; in view of those possibilities, this willingness to take risks with reactors is not encouraging. In terms of dispersal of radioactive wastes, however, we are dealing with what, in the light of past years' experience, we can consider a virtual certainty. The problems of Humboldt will be repeated, and reactors will continue to function just barely within AEC limits. This means an enormously increased discharge of radiation to air and water in the next few years. Most of the reactors presently planned are ten to twelve times as large as Humboldt. Total discharges of waste will be proportionately greater. More than seventy of these mammoth plants are scheduled to go into operation within the next seven years, and dozens more will follow.

Nor are reactors themselves the only — or even the worst — source of radioactive pollution in the atomic power industry.

The fuel for reactors undergoes a complex series of extractions and transformations over a course of years. Uranium ore is mined, and the uranium is extracted and shipped to a chemical plant, where the extracted ore, called "yellow-cake" from its appearance, is converted into uranium hexafluoride, which is then shipped to one of the government's huge gas diffusion plants at Oak Ridge, Tennessee; Portsmouth, Ohio; or Paducah, Kentucky. Here the content of fissionable uranium 235 is increased, or "enriched." The product is then shipped to a series of other plants, where it is converted to uranium oxide, compacted into small pellets, packed into long tubes which are assembled into finished fuel elements. The finished fuel is shipped to a reactor where it is used; but this is by no means the end of its travels. After wastes, or fission products, have accumulated in the fuel to the point where it is no longer usable, it is stored for a while, and then shipped to a reprocessing plant. Here the radioactive wastes are extracted, and the depleted uranium and small amounts of plutonium are recovered. The reclaimed uranium may be shipped to a chemical plant to rebegin the fuel cycle. The plutonium is sold to the government; the extracted wastes are either discharged to the air and water, or packaged and shipped to a storage or burial site.

At every step in this long path, there is some release of radiation to the environment. Some of the releases are known and controlled; some are unforeseen or, in some cases, ignored.

Radiation problems in the reactor industry therefore begin in the shafts of uranium mines. Uranium ore also contains radium and other radioactive substances; radium, in the process of slow decomposition, releases radon, which is a gas. When the ore is mined, radon gas and its own decomposition products accumulate in the mine shaft and pose a severe hazard to miners. The first disastrous effects of radon gas were observed in the 1930's in mining communities in the Erzgebirge Mountains; the mining area is called Schneeberg in Germany and Joachimstal in Czechoslovakia. A study performed between

1935 and 1939 revealed that approximately half the deaths among miners were due to lung cancer, and that 80 percent of the remaining deaths were due to other lung diseases.[14]

Shortly after the Second World War, great efforts were made by the Atomic Energy Commission to encourage exploration and uranium mining in the United States; by the early 1950's vast deposits in the West and Southwest had been uncovered. The United States Public Health Service, aware of the studies of European mines, surveyed the domestic situation. Four hundred air samples were taken from 75 mines; most samples showed radioactivity which far exceeded standards set by the International and National Commissions on Radiation Protection. These results were reported in 1955, and the International Labor Organization commented that they "give cause for considerable disquiet." [15]

Nothing, however, was done. By 1960, there were 1,000 active underground mines, but the AEC had no jurisdiction over them and the state and federal agencies which did seemed unaware of the problem. The problem was not brought to national attention until the summer of 1967. On April 26, 1967, Leo Goodman of the Industrial Union Department of the AFL-CIO, who has for many years been watchdog of the nuclear industry, addressed a meeting of the American Public Health Association. Goodman recounted the long history of evidence of hazards and complete inaction in uranium mining, and stated that the Colorado Industrial Mining Commission had paid a number of claims to the families of miners who had died of lung cancer. He pointed out that, in 1956, the Public Health Service had issued a report which concluded that "Surveys of the Colorado Plateau uranium mines have shown that 65 percent of the miners were exposed to concentrations of radon and its daughters [decay products] comparable to those reported to exist earlier in European mines." [16] Some of the mines surveyed had as much as 59 times the permissible level of radiation.

Following Goodman's speech and a number of newspaper stories which appeared at about the same time, the Department of Labor suddenly exercised its authority to set protective standards. Protests from the Joint Committee on Atomic Energy and uranium mining companies that the standards were too stringent and perhaps unenforceable resulted in a series of congressional hearings and a certain amount of acrimonious debate. After some weeks, a standard (the more lenient one recommended by the Federal Radiation Council) was finally accepted. Evidence adduced by Joint Committee hearings showed that the standard adopted would result in some increase in the rate of lung cancer among miners, beyond that in the general population; the additional cancer deaths would not be so many as to be easily distinguishable from those of other causes, but that there would be some additional deaths seemed generally accepted. [17]

Although the AEC published its first price schedule for uranium in 1948, it was not until July of 1967 that a safety standard of any sort for uranium miners was enforceable. All this despite the record of disastrous experience in European uranium mines. A very similar pattern can be seen in the history of radioactive water pollution from uranium mines.

Twelve million tons of radioactive sand, the refuse of uranium mining in the Colorado River Basin, is heaped in largely untended piles in an area affecting at least seven states in the Southwest. For nearly twenty years these sands have been accumulating, being blown by the wind into neighboring communities, and being washed by the rain into the tributaries of the Colorado River and eventually into Lake Mead: a water system which provides water for drinking and irrigation to parts of California, Nevada, Utah, Wyoming, Colorado, New Mexico and Arizona.

In the late 1950's the magnitude of the pollution hazard from uranium mining was discovered by the Public Health Service. Concentrations of radium 226 in algae in one river were as high as 3560 picocuries per kilogram. Alfalfa harvested in the area showed a high of 1160 picocuries per kilogram. Water in the San Miguel River reached 88 picocuries per liter during 1955. We can compare these figures to the maximum permissible concentration established by the Public Health Service of three picocuries per liter for drinking water. The Federal Water Pollution Control Administration estimated that up to 1959, people drinking water from the Animas River received three times the maximum permissible exposure from radium 226 and strontium 90 (from fallout).[18]

Once alerted to the hazard, the PHS began pressing for control of wastes from the uranium mills in the area, and much progress was made. Wastes are no longer dumped directly into neighboring streams and certain of the discharges of the mills have been halted, but the huge quantities of refuse produced by the processing of uranium ore remain a problem. For every ton of uranium ore passing through the mills, only about five pounds of salable uranium oxide is produced. The remainder, which resembles sand, is called "tailings" and is heaped near the mills.

In the early 1960's the Atomic Energy Commission cut back considerably its requirements for uranium, and a number of mills in the Colorado Basin were closed down. At the mills which closed, the radioactive tailings produced during their operation were simply abandoned. About three million tons of such abandoned tailings have been slowly blowing and washing away, producing further contamination of the Colorado River watershed. Some of the enormous heaps of tailings are directly on the banks of rivers and are being slowly washed away and deposited in the reservoirs of Lake Mead and Lake Powell, which supply water to a large part of the Southwest.

On May 6, 1966, the Subcommittee on Air and Water Pollution of the Committee on Public Works of the United States Senate held hearings on "Radioactive Water Pollution in the Colorado River Basin." The chairman of the Subcommittee was Senator Edmund S. Muskie of Maine, who has a continuing interest in problems of water pollution. The day's hearing was based on a report in March of 1965 by the Federal Water Pollution Control Administration, which has maintained a continuing effort to curtail pollution in this area.

Two thousands grams of radium 226 are present in the abandoned tailings piles. (Hazardous quantities of radium are usually measured in trillionths of a gram.) A larger amount of radium is presumably present in the tailings at operating mill sites. There is, in addition, an unknown quantity of radioactive thorium and lead, but the radium is considered the most serious problem. It is probably the most damaging of all radioactive isotopes, accumulating in the bone where it causes cancer and other diseases. The maximum permissible concentration established for radium is the lowest of any isotope. The FWPCA estimates that if ten tons from one of the tailings piles slips into an adjacent river (a not unlikely event), the concentration of radium 226 in the river water might go as high as 70 picograms per liter within the first hour. This compares to a maximum permissible concentration of three picograms per liter. If a larger slippage occurred in the abandoned piles — an event which has occurred in the past at operating mills, dumping as much as 120 tons of tailings into the river — levels of radium in the river water would remain above the maximum permissible concentration for days afterward.

Testifying before Senator Muskie's subcommittee, Dr. Peter Morris, Director, Division of Operational Safety, AEC, stated that "there is currently no significant hazard associated with uranium milling activities in the Colorado River Basin." He also stated that "we do not think that data available at this time support the conclusion that there is longterm radiological hazard." [19] This statement contradicted the FWPCA report which found "the Federal Water Pollution Control Administration is concerned with the potential problems that appear to be associated with the tailings because of their extremely long-lived radioactivity." [20] The half-life of radium 226 is 1620 years; the half-life of thorium 230, also present in the tailings, is 80,000 years.

Much of the area affected by contamination from the mills is also an area of high fallout from the Nevada test site. Murray Stein, chief of the enforcement program of FWPCA, testified as follows: "We found, when we first got into the area of the Colorado River Basin, that people were being exposed to several times the maximum permissible limit of radioactivity. The source at that time was, or course, fallout."

In other words, the same population which in the past has been exposed to high levels of radioactivity from fallout and from dumping of wastes from uranium mills continues to be subjected to exposure from erosion of the tailings piles. There has been no attempt to determine what total exposure people have actually received. About 25,000 people on the Animas River in New Mexico probably have received the most severe exposures.

While maintaining that the radiation hazard did not warrant control measures, the AEC had not opposed the proposal from the FWPCA for reducing erosion in the abandoned tailings piles by covering them with gravel and establishing vegetation. No plant life will grow in the uncovered tailings. The FWPCA considers that reduction of erosion is an interim measure of control to allow the government and the mill owners to agree on the methods and the responsibility for permanent disposal of the wastes. This is liable to be a difficult problem. About 30 million tons of tailings have accumulated in various parts of the country, and the total, of course, is growing. A single mill processes several thousand tons of uranium ore each day, the vast bulk of which is returned to the environment as radioactive waste.

In the summer of 1967, a conference was held among the concerned parties at Denver, Colorado, and some interim control measures, including erosion control, were agreed to. A study is presently under way to determine the extent of release of radioactive gases (radon and its products) from the tailings piles. As in the case of the miners, the remedy, partial in any case, was proposed 20 years after the problem had been created.

Similar problems occur at every point along the long uranium fuel cycle. Potentially the most serious by far of these occurs at the fuel-processing plant.

The fragments of fissioned atoms, radioactive wastes, slowly accumulate in reactor fuel. After a period of time, enough wastes accumulate to extinguish the chain reaction going on in the fuel, as ashes may smother a fire. Before this point is reached, the fuel must be removed from the reactor and the radioactive "ashes" extracted. This is a more difficult and dangerous operation than it seems. It must be borne in mind that it is precisely these radioactive wastes which constitute the radiation hazard in the civilian atomic energy program. Uranium fuel elements, before they have been placed in a reactor, are nearly harmless, and may be held in a bare hand. After undergoing a slow, controlled chain reaction in the reactor for several months, however, the same fuel element becomes the most hazardous object, short of an atomic bomb, known to man. It can only be transported in enormous lead and steel casks weighing many tons, and contains within it enough radioactivity, if distributed, to poison whole cities.

This enormous hazard derives from the violently radioactive fragments of split atoms, fission products. These are a bewildering array of radioactive twins of common elements, and range from a form of radioactive nitrogen with a half-life of just over seven seconds to iodine 129 with a half-life of more than 17 million years.

When a fuel assembly has been in a reactor for its allotted time, it is lifted out of the reactor core with remote-control equipment and lowered into a pool of water within the reactor building itself. Here it is stored for several weeks, to allow the shorter-lived radioactive elements to decay. This reduces the hazard in handling, and also lowers the temperature of the fuel element (even when removed from the reactor, the fuel assembly is so hot, and remains so for months, that it would melt unless artificially cooled). Two of the fission products have become familiar to the public, as they are also (and for the same reasons) among the principal hazards in fallout from bomb testing: strontium 90 and cesium 137. Both have half-lives near 30 years, and hence will not decay appreciably over any feasible period of storage. Tritium, a radioactive relative of hydrogen with a half-life of 12 years, is also present, although in far smaller amounts; like radioactive cesium and strontium, tritium is readily taken up by living things. Iodine 131 is still more biologically active but shorter-lived. Its close relative, iodine 129, lasts a far longer time, although present in far smaller quantities. The other fission product of concern is one we have already encountered, krypton 85, the noble gas which was being released in such surprising quantities from the Humboldt Bay reactor.

After a period of storage, the fuel assembly is loaded, again by remote control, into a massive lead-and-steel "shipping cask." This enormous cylinder, ten feet or more high, contains its own cooling system. The shipping cask is loaded onto a truck and shipped to a fuel-reprocessing plant which may be hundreds of miles from the reactor itself. Until very recently, the AEC did all fuel reprocessing at its own plants at Savannah River, near Aiken, South Carolina, and at the National Reactor Testing Station, near Idaho Falls, Idaho. In 1966, the first private fuel-reprocessing facility was dedicated at West Valley, about 30 miles south of Buffalo, New York. It is owned by Nuclear Fuel Services, Inc., which in turn is owned (principally) by W. R. Grace and Company. Several other such private plants are planned for the near future, principally by the reactor manufacturers. Construction will soon begin on such a plant in Marion, Illinois, to be owned by General Electric.

Having traveled perhaps halfway across the country, the fuel assembly is again stored for a time in a deep pool of water, along with other fuel elements which are waiting their turn for processing. In storage, shipping, and storage again, great care must be taken that fuel assemblies are not bunched together in a critical mass — one which could sustain a chain reaction. Once out of the reactor, no control of the fission process is possible, and such an event could lead to melting of the fuel and release of radioactivity. Since the neutrons which sustain a chain reaction can travel a considerable distance through air or water, fuel assemblies must be well separated.

The fuel processing is carried out entirely automatically or by remote control, in massive concrete chambers, because of the intense radioactivity of the fuel. First, the assembly is transferred from the storage pool to a chamber in which its external fittings are removed, leaving only a bundle of fuel rods, each less than an inch thick and several feet long. These rods are then chopped into sections a few inches long, and dumped into a nitric acid bath which dissolves the uranium and fission products, but leaves the steel jackets intact. The acid solution containing the fuel and wastes is then piped into a series of chambers in which the complex process of chemical separations is carried out. These in essence consist of passing the water-and-acid solution of fuel and wastes past a flow of organic solvent moving in the opposite direction; by delicately adjusting conditions, different substances may be forced to pass from one fluid to the other, and are thereby separated.

Uranium and plutonium are extracted, and separated from each other, and further purified. The uranium may eventually find its way back into reactor fuel, after passing through a series of chemical, enrichment and fabrication plants; the plutonium will be turned over to the government for storage, against the time that it may be used as reactor fuel in future designs.

The nitric acid solution which remains contains most of the

fission wastes and, hence, is intensely radioactive; this liquid is concentrated to reduce its volume, and then pumped into huge underground storage tanks. These tanks must be cooled, for the heat produced by the radioactivity in the wastes raises the temperature of the liquid far past the boiling point, and if allowed to accumulate would soon rupture the tanks. Cooling is accomplished by passing steam from the tanks into a condenser above ground. The tanks themselves are huge, holding 750,000 gallons each, and are stirred continuously with compressed air to keep radioactive solids from settling to the bottom.

The wastes in these tanks pose a singularly difficult problem. The quantities of radioactivity in them are simply staggering. For instance, the maximum permissible concentration of strontium 90 in drinking water is a few billionths of a curie per gallon, yet the wastes in storage contain on average about 100 curies per gallon. There are now something like 65 million gallons of hot waste in storage in the AEC's "tank farms" or atomic graveyards, more than enough to poison all the water on earth. The half-life of strontium 90 is a little over 27 years: it will be many centuries, therefore, before the wastes in storage will have decayed to tolerable levels.

These boiling hot wastes must therefore be stirred and cooled for generations. This is clearly an unsatisfactory method of operation, to put it mildly, and was recognized as such from the earliest days of the atomic program. Weapon production needs in the forties and fifties, which created most of the wastes now in storage, could not be delayed while a satisfactory solution to the waste-disposal problem was found. Now, twenty years after the fact, the AEC is experimenting with a process which gives promise of being a feasible disposal method. In project Salt Vault, the liquid wastes are reduced to a relatively inert solid form which is not easily dissolved in water; the most promising method is to produce a kind of glass, which is then encased in a sealed steel container. This container is stored for a time, and is then transported to a large abandoned salt mine, or natural or artificial cavern in a deep salt deposit. The point of using salt caverns is that they are quite impervious to water, and have been dry for millennia and can be expected to remain so for a comparable period of time. Once disposed of in salt caverns, therefore, radioactive wastes could be expected to stay put.

This seems to be a reasonable disposal method for the most highly radioactive wastes which will be formed in the future; it rather aggravates another, and in the long run perhaps more serious, problem, however.

At the fuel reprocessing plant, the stainless steel jackets of the fuel elements are broken open, and the fuel itself dissolved in nitric acid. Radioactive gases which had until then been trapped in the fuel are released. These include large volumes of noble gases, especially krypton 85, and radioactive iodine. Within the sealed air-circulation system of the reprocessing plant, these gases are scrubbed and filtered, to remove any solid particles and to capture as much of the highly dangerous radioactive iodine as possible. The remaining gases are then discharged to the outside, being mixed with large volumes of air at the same time.

This is essentially the same procedure used for discharging controlled amounts of radioactivity from reactors, and in fact the reprocessing plant in this respect resembles a reactor in which all the fuel elements have ruptured and released their radioactive contents. The krypton 85 which was not released from the Humboldt reactor itself is eventually released at a fuel reprocessing plant.

The same standards which apply to reactors apply to fuel processing plants: they may release unlimited quantities of radioactivity as long as it is sufficiently diluted and poses no *direct* hazard to people in the surrounding area. It is estimated that by the year 2000 more than one billion curies of krypton will have accumulated,[21] and all of this staggering quantity of radioactivity will be released into the air, permanently beyond control. Eventually, it is likely that all of the presently allowable exposure of the general population to radioactivity from whatever source will be exhausted by exposure to krypton 85 in the air.

A similar problem exists with radioactive tritium, which is a twin of hydrogen. This is a weakly radioactive substance with a half-life of about 12 years and is produced in small quantities in reactor fuel. Nearly all the tritium in fuel is presently discharged from reprocessing plants in waste water, along with a number of other dilute radioactive substances. By the year 2000, there will be an accumulation of something like 36 million curies of this substance knocking around.[22] Unlike the noble gases, tritium is easily incorporated into living tissue.

Other isotopes will follow similar patterns of buildup in the environment. This burden will be increased by the disposal methods proposed for higher-level wastes. If the hot liquid wastes from reprocessing plants are to be solidified, they will be heated and treated chemically in yet another plant, and the result will be a new series of releases of low-level liquid and gaseous wastes which, if present methods continue, will be released to the environment.

Although mines, reactors and chemical plants are the most visible sources of radioactive pollution, they are by no means the only ones.

At every stage of the fuel cycle, radioactive materials are being shipped from one place to another — from mine to processing plant to enrichment plant to reactor to fuel reprocessing, and so on. Soon it seems likely that a new step will be added: the transportation of high-level liquid wastes from reprocessing plants to other plants, like the pilot installation now in operation at Hanford, for converting the radioactive liquid wastes into more easily stored solids. Particularly in some stages, this transportation process is quite hazardous.

The most ticklish problem to date has been the shipment of irradiated fuel elements — fuel after it has been in a reactor for some time, and has been removed for the extraction of wastes. Such fuel is generally shipped by truck or railroad. Only one or two fuel assemblies are generally shipped at any one time — which is understandable enough, since the shipping "cask" for one element may weigh as much as 70 tons. A typical cask will be a cylinder three feet in diameter and ten feet high, with a foot-thick inner wall of lead shielding. As mentioned earlier, the cask typically has its own cooling system to keep the temperature of the fuel assembly below the melting point.

A truck or train accident which would breach the shipping cask could be a disaster, and therefore the cask is carefully designed to withstand severe impacts and high temperatures. A really severe accident, perhaps followed by a sustained fire, could conceivably lead to breaking open the container and exposing the fuel, and this might happen in a populous area. More likely, however, is the release of radioactivity from such an accident into surface water which eventually finds its way into human use.

The prospects of such a catastrophic shipping accident have

been discussed for years within the AEC. In 1958, Dr. Harold Knapp, then of the AEC, delivered a paper in which he noted that the Safety and Fire Protection Branch of the AEC believed that for some transportation accidents "costs of several million dollars would be credible." [23] Using available statistics for truck and train accidents, Dr. Knapp went on to calculate the likelihood of serious radioactivity accidents, and conclude that, "Very roughly one might expect a serious accident every 100 million vehicle miles of shipment for ordinary methods of transport." In 1962, it was estimated that shipments of reactor fuel wastes to burial grounds already totaled 2 million miles per year; this figure is probably larger now and will continue to grow.[24]

It should be emphasized that radioactive materials are shipped on common carriers — that is, the same railway, barge and truck concerns which handle other commercial shipping, and are transported according to rules for hazardous materials such as explosives, where the radiation level seems to warrant this. Packages containing small amounts of radioactivity, as for instance isotope packages for research or medical use, are simply shipped or sent through the mails like any other parcel.

The risk of catastrophic accident in transportation, as in reactor operation, is low. Dr. Knapp points out that "One hundred shipments per year of 1000 miles each with present rail accident rates would mean a serious accident as defined here every 800 years, on the average. Should the rate of shipment go as high as 10,000 shipments per year, the average time between serious accidents would come down to 8 years." [25] The number of shipments of irradiated fuel elements is expected to be at the lower end of this range for several years, but will obviously increase as the reactor program enlarges. Dr. J. W. Morgan commented, at a conference on this subject in 1962:

"It is quite possible that some time in the future there will be an accident that could be described as catastrophic. Whether we describe it as catastrophic on a dollar basis or on the basis of persons involved who may be injured, that is something else, but I think it would be interesting to look at this whole thing on a task force basis." [26]

Truck and train accidents happen regularly and predictably. As the volume of shipments goes up, the risk of serious accidents actually happening increases steadily each year. Most accidents, of course, are far short of catastrophe, and result only in the release of relatively small quantities of radioactivity. At the same conference in 1962 at which Dr. Morgan was expressing the above trepidations, another report recounted the 47 accidents which the AEC had had to date; only 17 were considered "serious." [27]

Radioactivity releases within the AEC's operations are not always so easily identified, as much of the Commission's work is highly classified. The operations of the Hanford and Savannah River reactors, used for producing plutonium for weapons, are not public knowledge, although some items are released from time to time. It is known that several thousand curies of radioactive zinc, chromium and other "activated corrosion products" are released to the Columbia River each year. Other releases at Hanford are less well known. For instance, a recent authoritative and exhaustive compilation of public information regarding radiation accidents lists the following incident:

45. *Location:* Hanford, Washington
Date: 21 December, 1959
Nature of Incident: Fuel element rupture in a reactor resulting in contamination of desert. Such ruptures are considered routine and minor releases of radioactivity occur perhaps once or twice a year.[28]

No explanation of the term "minor" is given. Entry no. 69 gives even less information:

Location: Hanford, Washington
Date: 7 June, 1957
Nature of Incident: Uranium dissolver explosion.

or item 70 also at Hanford, the following year:

Nature of Incident: Purex plant explosion.

These were apparently both accidents in fuel-reprocessing plants, and therefore could conceivably have resulted in considerable release of radioactivity, but no further details are given. These examples could be multiplied almost indefinitely.

Although a detailed picture is almost impossible to draw, it is clear that the sources of radioactivity being added to our environment are growing rapidly in number and size. As twenty years ago it was quite clear that there would eventually be a problem of radioactive wastes from uranium mines, and severe risks to miners, so at present we can see that eventually there will be serious problems with the disposal of radioactive wastes. In mining, in transportation, in reactor operation, fuel reprocessing and storage, there will be small losses or intentional releases of radiation, in each case designed to avoid killing anyone nearby. But the radioactivity will not go away. It is in our surroundings, and will accumulate in living things until the point of severe damage is reached; nothing in the present reactor program indicates that there will be a way of halting releases before that point.

VII

THE COMING THING

AT THE TIME OF THIS WRITING, plans are being made to reactivate the $120 million Enrico Fermi atomic power plant, on the shore of Lake Erie between Detroit and Toledo. Built in spite of bitter opposition and plagued by a series of technical failures, this nuclear plant, in 1966, suffered an accident that might have just missed being a disaster. Designed to produce electric power and plutonium for nuclear weapons, the plant has never produced usable amounts of either; as a prototype of the next generation of atomic power plants, its failure may have serious implications for the future of civilian nuclear power. Plans to start it up again may mean further accidents which might endanger nearby cities.

In 1956, when the Power Reactor Development Corporation first proposed building the Fermi reactor at Lagoona Beach, Michigan, atomic electric power was still a new idea. The first nuclear plant to produce commercial electric power — at Shippingport, Pennsylvania — was a year away from its opening. A dozen years later, and after far wider acceptance of atomic energy, the Fermi reactor continues to be a controversial facility, and a source of grave concern. The debate has a history as old as the reactor itself; in 1957, Senator Clinton Anderson of New Mexico made the following remarks toward the end of an ad-

dress to the Second Annual Convention of the New Mexico
AFL-CIO:

> Yes, I have found it necessary to urge labor unions to intervene
> against the action of the Atomic Energy Commission in granting
> a permit for the construction of the Lagoona Beach reactor next
> to the City of Detroit. . . . I telephoned not only the Governor
> of the State of Michigan, but I called labor unions and said to them
> that here was a reactor being built next to a metropolitan area
> where workers in other factories would be subjected to the harm-
> ful radiation effects if there should be a breakdown in the La-
> goona reactor. I felt that we should not permit the reactor to be
> constructed until we knew it to be safe.[1]

Senator Anderson apparently was concerned because the
Atomic Energy Commission, in going ahead with the Fermi
reactor, acted despite a report from its own Advisory Committee on Reactor Safeguards, which was at best noncommittal
about the safety of proceeding. Several unions responded to
Anderson's plea, and extended litigation began. A federal court
voided the license which the AEC had granted for construction
of the reactor, but the Supreme Court, in a divided decision,
reversed the lower court's action — and construction resumed.
Justice Douglas, with Justice Black concurring, worded a very
strong dissent, called the AEC's interpretation of the Atomic
Energy Act "a light-hearted approach to the most awesome, the
most deadly, the most dangerous process that man has ever
conceived." [2]

Why so much controversy over this particular reactor? Fermi
was to be the prototype of what industry still feels is going to
be the coming thing in reactors, the "sodium-cooled fast
breeder," in the jargon of the trade. And in spite of Fermi's

near disastrous failure, all reactor manufacturers hope to begin construction on new fast breeder prototypes by about 1970. By 1980, some firms hope to have full-scale commercial power plants under construction; eventually, it is believed, this and other advanced reactor types will completely replace the current form of reactor.

This optimism is based chiefly on the hope of lowered fuel costs in the fast breeder. Fuel costs in the present commercial atomic plants may be as much as or more than the cost of the reactor itself; the fast breeder, on the other hand, may eventually burn plutonium it has itself produced instead of the very expensive uranium 235 used in other commercial reactors.

Most modern reactors use a design very different from that of the Fermi plant. In a typical reactor, such as the Quad-Cities plant in Illinois on the Mississippi River, uranium 235 and uranium 238 are mixed in tiny pellets which are packed into metal tubes about a half-inch thick and several feet long. These long, delicate rods are then arranged in rectangular packages about five inches wide and fourteen feet long; 724 of these "subassemblies" are put together to form the core of the reactor. Such a core contains 362,000 pounds of uranium oxide.

This enormous mass of uranium is at a temperature of 1000°F. Millions of gallons of water flow through the core, between the long, thin fuel elements, cooling it; the water boils immediately and steam is drawn off from the core to turn a turbine, which can produce 715,000 kilowatts of electricity, enough power to supply a city of one million.

Within the core of the reactor, the nuclei of uranium 235 atoms are fissioning; when a nucleus shatters, it produces typically two or three neutrons. Some neutrons may collide repeatedly with the atoms of water flowing through the core until their speed is slowed by a factor of thousands. The slowed neutrons may then be absorbed by other nuclei of uranium 235, which absorb slow neutrons much more easily than the fast ones.

Other neutrons may escape from the reactor entirely or may be absorbed unproductively by uranium 238, uranium 235, the cooling water, the metal walls of the fuel element, or any of the many impurities present in the fuel and the reactor materials.

Still other neutrons may be absorbed by the nucleus of uranium 238 in such a fashion that it is then converted to plutonium.

After months of operation, the fuel is removed from the reactor and transported to a processing plant, where it is dissolved in acid and the plutonium and impurities are removed. Ideally, the recovered plutonium can be used to make new reactor fuel; this is what happens in a "breeder" reactor. Unfortunately, in the kind of reactor just described, typical of those now being built, far less fuel is made than is burned.

This is because only two or three neutrons are produced in each uranium fission. One must be used to keep the chain reaction going. If one escapes or is captured unproductively, then there are simply not enough neutrons available to convert uranium 238 to plutonium at the desired rate. The Fermi reactor is an attempt to solve this problem.

In the Quad-Cities reactor, the cooling water will act also as a moderator, slowing down the neutrons. In Fermi, the moderator is removed and the neutrons are not slowed. At higher neutron speeds, "unproductive" capture by U-235 and plutonium is reduced. More neutrons are available for transforming U-238 into plutonium, so that more plutonium is produced than the uranium 235 that has been burned. The reactor has then been able to "breed" fuel and is called a breeder reactor. In theory, one and one half pounds of fuel could be produced for each pound burned.

Fermi achieves further conservation of neutrons by making the core highly compact, with a very high percentage of fissionable material (uranium 235 or plutonium) in the fuel. This further acts to maintain the high energy of the neutrons. The compact core is surrounded by a "blanket" of uranium 238 which is slowly converted to plutonium. A "fast breeder" reactor core which produced as much power as the Quad-Cities plant might be only four or five feet high, instead of fourteen or fifteen.

Because it is so much more compact, the fast reactor must be cooled by a more efficient cooling medium than water; liquid sodium is usually used, although this is very difficult and hazardous material to handle, as it burns in air or water.

When fast breeders were first designed, it was thought that uranium was a scarce element, and this was an added factor in making them attractive. Subsequent explorations have uncovered vast reserves of uranium in this country, in Canada, and elsewhere. For a time, in fact, uranium exploration ran far ahead of the demand, and in the early years of this decade a number of mines had to be closed, and the AEC accumulated stockpiles far in excess of its needs in order to prevent complete collapse of the uranium mining industry which had developed. The present rash of reactor orders, coming unexpectedly, has created a sudden new demand which may strain the present supply, but new exploration is again being conducted with something of the heat of the earlier uranium rush, and supplies will probably keep pace with demand, whether or not fast breeders are developed to conserve uranium. Some predict a

rise in uranium prices, as reactor expansion outstrips new mining of high-grade ores, but this could easily be offset by an eas-
ing of import restrictions, by release of the AEC's stockpile, or
by advances in mining or extraction technology which would
make lower-grade ores available. A recent industry-sponsored
study concludes: "Sufficient uranium is available in known deposits to permit electric power companies to proceed with plans
for additional (water-moderated) power reactors for a number
of years ahead. The results of current exploration efforts should
become apparent well before 1971. . . ." [3]

With these vast new reserves, it was possible to give emphasis to the presently popular water-moderated reactors which
burn much more fuel than they produce; despite their uneco-
nomical use of fuel, water cooled and moderated reactors are
far more easy to build and operate safely and reliably — and
are far cheaper in terms of initial cost.

Revenue from the sale of plutonium for weapons had originally been expected to offset the high building and design costs
of the Fermi plant; eventually, if the design succeeded, plutonium would also be sold for fuel in other reactors. But the government's demand for plutonium has slackened considerably,
as the arms race has slowed, and can be met at government
plants in Richland, Washington, and Aiken, South Carolina.

Despite the apparent abundance of uranium to fuel water-
cooled reactors and the absence of the expected demand for
plutonium, and in the face of the dramatic failure of the Fermi
reactor, fast reactors are again being proposed. At a meeting
of the American Nuclear Society in San Francisco, April 10–12,
1967, several firms in this country, Great Britain, France, Italy
and Germany unveiled plans for various types of fast reactors;
the British seem to have the lead in this field, and their proto-

type is already being built and is expected to be operating by 1970. The U.S.S.R. is also building a prototype, and Russian scientists were expected at the meeting but did not appear.

The reason for this resurgent interest is economic; fast breeders may burn the plutonium they themselves produce, obviating the need for enriched uranium 235 fuel which contributes so much to the cost of present commercial reactors. An additional factor is that only the United States, the U.S.S.R., China, Britain and France have the capability to separate the uranium isotopes; other countries wishing to develop nuclear power are therefore dependent on foreign supplies of fuel unless they can develop plutonium producing and burning reactors. This is probably an important factor in the German and Italian programs.

Yet, despite their possible economic advantage over the presently used water reactors, fast reactors pose serious safety problems. In November 1954, a conference was held in the offices of the Detroit Edison Company, attended by some of the most prominent physicists in the country. The proceedings of this conference were classified by the AEC. It was devoted in part to a discussion of the problems which had arisen in the operation of the Experimental Breeder Reactor I, the prototype of the Enrico Fermi reactor. There was considerable discussion during the conference of the possibility that an accident would cause the highly dangerous uranium 235 core to reassemble in a "prompt critical" configuration — one which would undergo rapid and uncontrolled chain reaction like that in a nuclear weapon. At one point, Dr. Zinn, who headed the design of EBR-I, said:

If you do melt the central section of the reactor and it runs down the tubes as Dr. Bethe suggested, does this give you an increase in reactivity which is greater than the amount that you can subtract with your control rods? . . . If you couldn't do it with your rods, you would be in bad shape.

Chairman Bethe: Right. I suppose it would increase the reactivity some.[4]

At another point in the conference, the question of fuel melting or warping to create a more critical configuration was brought up again, and the chairman of the conference, Dr. Hans Bethe, asked,

Suppose that it did. What would happen?

Dr. Zinn: It is very probable, when it does that, it will disassemble the machine.[5]

"Disassemble the machine" was a euphemism for a small nuclear explosion. By the end of the conference everyone was agreed that such an event, particularly if for some reason the fuel melted, and subsequently ran together in a more dangerous configuration, was possible, and that the fast reactor was so new and complex that all the possible causes of such an accident could not be foreseen.

Some at the conference expressed the opinion that a prototype fast reactor should be built in a remote location before a commercial plant was attempted. This point of view was also put forward by AEC Commissioner Willard Libby at the 1955 "Section 202" hearings before the Joint Committee. Commissioner Libby said that the construction of a fast breeder in a populated zone "requires that the safety of this type of reactor be determined experimentally . . . by construction of a reasonably similar prototype in an isolated area."

This approach was opposed by another at the conference, which eventually won out: The way to build fast reactors would be to provide them with containment structures which could resist the force of an explosion and so keep radiation, in the event of an accident, from reaching the outside and the public.

The fears as to the possibility of a serious accident in a fast reactor were partly justified a year after this secret conference. In November of 1955, an experiment was conducted in the AEC's experimental breeder reactor (EBR-I), to identify the source of an unsafe characteristic: a "positive temperature co-efficient." The reactor was to be run briefly with the coolant (an alloy of sodium and potassium) shut off. The operator was instructed to shut off the reactor with the fast shut-down rods, but instead used the slower control rods. The reactor did not shut down, but instead the power went on increasing. Safety measures were instituted, but despite these procedures, the temperature within the core rose within seconds to more than 2000°F. The fuel and its steel cladding in the center of the core melted:

> . . . contact with coolant eventually chilled and froze the mass [of molten uranium 235], blocking further downward movement. . . . The melted and refrozen material . . . formed a pot of sorts which tended to hold and collect the materials [fuel and cladding] falling from the upper part of the core. . . . Partially melted rods from above apparently dropped into the eutectic mass below.[6]

Fortunately, no serious damage to persons resulted from this accident; the reactor core was damaged beyond repair. It was demonstrated quite clearly, however, that when an accident in a fast reactor caused a meltdown of fuel, the U-235 could collect in fairly large quantities in one place. In a very large reactor, this could have catastrophic implications. In 1965, a conference on fast breeder technology was again held at Argonne Laboratories, and the record of those discussions shows that there was still no agreement on how serious the resultant explosion might be in a given reactor, nor were the participants sure that the possible causes of such an accident were all known. Yet in January of 1966, the Enrico Fermi reactor, the only commercial fast breeder ever built, after years of malfunction, was run up to full power for the first time; by October of that year, it had suffered a serious accident.[7]

In October of 1966, preparations were made to restart the Fermi plant, which had been shut down because of the latest in a long series of difficulties. The difficulty this time had been in the steam generator, where the heat carried by the sodium from the reactor is used to make steam. On the evening of October 4, 1966, the technicians in the control room in a separate building adjusted their controls, and control rods withdrew slightly from the faraway reactor core, hidden by tons of steel and concrete shielding.

By 11 P.M., the reactor was operating at a low power level; it was maintained at this level while the tons of sodium flowing through the core slowly heated to a temperature of 550°F. Instruments in the control room indicated that the reactor was operating normally. At eight o'clock the following morning, October 5, the operators of the reactor began the long and complex procedures which must precede operating the reactor at a higher power. The plan was to increase the heat being generated by the reactor, in order to test the newly-repaired steam generator and steam system.

A minor malfunction was found in a valve in the steam generator, and the program was delayed. At 1:45 P.M., the slow withdrawal of control rods to increase reactor power began again; within fifteen minutes, another small malfunction had appeared in a pump, and the reactor was damped again. A replacement pump was switched on, the slow increase in power began again. By 3 P.M., the reactor was producing 20,000 kilowatts of heat energy, still only a small fraction of its maximum capacity of 200,000 kilowatts.

At this point, the reactor operator noticed an abnormality in one of his instruments measuring the change in neutron production in the reactor core; the signal from the instrument became erratic. Reactors have their own personalities — the operator had observed this particular fluctuation in his instruments many times before, and often at the same time of day — 3 P.M. He ended automatic control of the reactor and switched to manual control for a while. The erratic signal disappeared, and automatic increase of reactor power began again.

Five minutes later, when the power level had reached 34,000 kilowatts, the erratic signal appeared again. A staff member present noticed that the control rods seemed to have been drawn farther out than was normal. Stepping to the back of the control panel, he examined the recorders which registered temperature at different points in the distant reactor core. At two points the temperature seemed higher than normal.

At almost the same moment, radiation alarms sounded from the reactor building and from detectors elsewhere in the plant. Automatic devices immediately sealed off the buildings in which the alarms had sounded; no personnel were present at the time.

By this time the power increase had halted; at 3:20 P.M., almost half an hour after the first abnormalities had been noticed, the reactor was scrammed — six safety rods were inserted their full distance, completely halting the chain reaction because of their absorption of neutrons.

The only visible signs of the accident were the abnormal meter readings in the control room and the automatic radiation alarms. High radiation levels were occurring in the plant buildings, but their cause was not known.

A meeting was held at the plant immediately. In order to try to determine what had happened, automatic samples of the liquid sodium coolant and of the argon gas in the sodium system were made (sodium reacts violently with air, and therefore the sodium system is filled with the inert gas, argon). Large amounts of radioactive fission products in these samples made it clear that a portion of the reactor fuel had melted. Once this had been established, there was great concern, for the possibility of further, and far more serious, accidents existed. Walter J. McCarthy, Jr., Assistant General Manager of the Power Reactor Development Corporation, who was present at this meeting, later stated that the possibility of such a secondary accident was "a terrifying thought." [8]

The long, thin fuel rods of the Fermi core contained about half a ton of uranium 235 — enough to make forty Hiroshima-sized atom bombs. These pins are arranged in 105 subassemblies, each composed of 140 pins. The sodium coolant must be pumped through the narrow gaps between fuel pins.

The cause of the accident was thought to be some interference with the flow of coolant among the fuel pins, and this has proved to be the case. In September of 1967, a specially designed forty-foot flexible periscope was wormed down through the reactor's innards and was used to sight, and then to photograph, a small object lying at the very bottom of the reactor. This object, which in early blurred photographs looked like a flattened beer can, has now been identified as a piece of crumpled sheet metal pulled loose from the reactor itself. On October 5, 1966, this object probably blocked one or two of the openings which admit cooling sodium to the reactor core. Within minutes, a large portion of the fuel in two subassemblies melted, and the assemblies themselves buckled, forcing nearby elements out of line. The reactor was apparently shut down in time to prevent severe damage to other portions of the fuel.[9]

It took more than a year to identify the cause of the accident. The presence of a crumpled bit of metal inside the delicate mechanism of the reactor seemed inexplicable. The mystery of its presence, and the difficulty of solving it, were not fully explained until February 5, 1968. Milton Shaw, Director of the AEC's reactor division, was testifying before the Joint Committee on Atomic Energy, explaining that within the previous week, the culpable piece of metal had been identified as a portion of the reactor itself. Congressman Craig Hosmer interrupted:

Now, there is more to the story, is there not?

Let me put it this way, then. I understand that late in the construction of the reactor, around 1959, the designers decided to cover the bottom of the vessel with a zirconium sheet as an added safeguard to prevent fuel melt from going through the bottom of the vessel, anticipating this Chinese syndrome. . . .

As we have seen, in case of an accident, the molten fuel might dissolve its way right through the reactor vessel, and anything beneath it, presumably "right down to China." The bottom of the Fermi reactor vessel was therefore coated with zirconium which, it was hoped, would hold the molten fuel. Projecting upward from the center of the zirconium sheet laid at the vessel's bottom was a cone about a foot high. During normal operation, the function of this cone was to direct the flow of coolant upward into the reactor core. During an accident, it was hoped, reactor fuel falling on this cone might be dispersed. The question arose of whether this cone should not also be covered with zirconium.

Representative Hosmer: Now, I understand that APDA (Atomic Power Development Associates), received from Al Amorosi a memo which said, in effect, that it would be easier to put zirc shrouds over the cone than to have to justify not doing so to the ACRS [Advisory Committee on Reactor Safeguards] when it came time for an operating license.

Is there such a memorandum in existence, to your knowledge?

Mr. Shaw: I understand there is, Mr. Hosmer, but your research staff seems to be much ahead of mine.

Representative Hosmer: Based on that, I understand that they hurriedly rounded up some zirconium sheet and fabricated these six triangular pieces, and they were bolted on the cone, maybe tack welded, I don't know, at least three bolts were used in each, and that the total cost of these sheets was about a hundred bucks.

Mr. Shaw: We understand that this was a last minute decision, hurriedly made, to put the zirconium pieces in.

We also understand that these additions were not shown on the final construction "as built" drawings. This became one of the problems related to identifying whether the object was part of the reactor or an object foreign to the reactor.

This again gets to the point that when you take shortcuts like this you must be prepared for the consequences.

In this case, the consequences were the accident of October 5, 1966, when one of the six triangular sheets of zirconium, less than a foot long, broke free of the flow-guide cone, and blocked the flow of coolant to a portion of the core.

In concluding this exchange, Mr. Hosmer put a final question:

One other thing I want to ask you, Mr. Shaw. In your judgment, was this cover on the flow regulator really needed, in the first place?

Mr. Shaw: I cannot answer that, Mr. Hosmer. . . . I think these are the kinds of engineering decisions that can go either way and still come out right.

Or wrong, one is tempted to add. The fast reactor seems to be the sort of mechanism in which the devices employed to forestall one sort of accident simply precipitate another. In any case, the Fermi reactor is now out of operation until at least the end of 1968, while its owners try to decide what to do about the remaining five triangles of zirconium, any one of which could break free and cause another, and perhaps more severe accident. Removing them will be inordinately difficult. And are they needed or not? The melting of fuel in a fast reactor is a disturbing risk.

The possibility that Walter McCarthy called a "terrifying thought" and that preoccupied the meeting after the accident was that a large quantity of fuel had melted and then recongealed when the reactor was shut down. Those at the meeting feared that enough uranium had recongealed so that a disturbance of the core — by an attempt to remove the damaged fuel, for example — would jar it into a critical mass too great to be controlled by the control rods, which were already at their maximum.

The result could have been an explosion — nowhere near as great as that of a nuclear weapon, but perhaps great enough to rupture the steel and concrete containment structure of the reactor. A large portion of the radioactive gases held within the core would then have been released to the atmosphere, and would have drifted uncontrolled with the wind. The huge quantities of radioactivity involved, and the proximity of Detroit, made such a prospect terrifying indeed.

No attempt was made to investigate the reactor core for a month, for fear of a second and more terrible accident. "It's one of those accidents the consequences [of which] are so terrible the probability has to be very very small," Walter McCarthy later said, describing the intensive study and calculation which went on during that month. When the operators of the reactor and the AEC felt assured that no further damage would occur, attempts to retrieve the damaged fuel were begun. To everyone's enormous relief, nothing did happen.

Some idea of the size of that relief can be gained by reading a report dated July, 1957, titled "A Report on the Possible Effects on the Surrounding Population of an Assumed Release of Fission Products into the Atmosphere from a 300 Megawatt [300,000 kilowatt] Nuclear Reactor Located at Lagoona Beach,

Michigan." This report was prepared at the Engineering Research Institute of the University of Michigan, for the Atomic Power Development Associates. APDA was the research, design and development organization established by the prospective owners and operators of the Enrico Fermi reactor; the membership of the latter (Power Reactor Development Corporation) and APDA were almost identical.

The report produced by APDA was very much like the AEC's WASH-740 report on the "Theoretical Consequences of Hypothetical Accidents." The two reports appeared at the same time, although each was prepared independently of the other. As in WASH-740, the APDA report did not delve very much into possible causes of an accident, but simply tried to ascertain the maximum possible damage to the surrounding population if a drastic accident were to occur. Unlike WASH-740, the APDA report considered a reactor in a specific location — the site of the Fermi plant. And unlike WASH-740, the APDA staff was willing to consider the worst conceivable circumstance, rather than those which seemed most likely. Thus the APDA report includes consideration of the case in which all of the radioactive wastes contained in the reactor fuel are released to the air, presumably after an explosion has burst the reactor's containment structures. WASH-740's worst case was the release of only 50 percent of fission products.

APDA also considered a range of weather conditions including the most highly unfavorable, a thermal inversion lasting for many hours, with a slow steady wind blowing radioactivity in the direction of the most populous areas of Detroit. These weather conditions were estimated to occur during about 5.4 days in each year. Assuming that these weather conditions prevailed at the time of the accident, and that the radioactive

cloud released from the reactor lost none of its virulence by
depositing fallout while it drifted, the report estimated these
damages:

One hundred and thirty-three thousand people would receive
fatal doses of radiation (450 roentgens or more); 181,000 would
receive immediate injuries (150 roentgens or more); 245,000
would receive doses which could result in long-term injury,
such as increased incidence of cancer, shortened lifetimes or
hereditary defects (25 roentgens or more). No attempt was
made to estimate property damage.[10]

It is constantly, and rightly, emphasized that the probability
of such a disastrous accident is low. This does not mean that
such an accident will not happen. Even one a hundred times
less severe — releasing only one percent of the reactor's accumulated wastes — could result in 420 deaths, according to
the APDA study. Accidents do happen, and it is in their nature
that their causes and consequences may not be entirely foreseen.

The accident which did happen at Fermi in 1966 is particularly disturbing when we examine the portion of the application
to construct the Fermi reactor called the "Hazards Summary
Report," prepared by the Power Reactor Development Company (PRDC), the consortium of public utilities and equipment
manufacturers which built and operates the Fermi reactor.[11]

As is required by the AEC, the Hazards Summary Report
contains a section describing the "maximum credible accident."
This is an attempt to specify an accident which is not expected
to occur, but which is the worst which the designers feel could
occur. Page 603.15 of the Hazards Summary states:

The maximum credible accident in the Fermi reactor is the melting of some or all of the fuel in one core subassembly, due to

either complete or partial plugging of the nozzle of that subassembly, or to a flow restriction within the subassembly. . . .

As a result of the October 5 accident, fuel in at least two subassemblies melted. Some damage was done to at least two other subassemblies.

The reactor would probably be shut down automatically as a result of the reactivity loss due to the melting of the fuel. . . .

This did not occur on October 5; the reactor was shut down manually.

. . . fission products . . . would have been released to the primary coolant system, and . . . the inert gas system. Since these systems are normally radioactive and sealed, there would be *no additional outward effect* caused by the addition of fission products from melted fuel [emphasis added].

In fact, there were outward effects, including high radiation levels in the reactor containment and fission product detection buildings. It is fortunate that there was leakage of radioactivity, for it was the sounding of radiation alarms which prompted the shutdown of the reactor. Had there been "no additional outward effect," the reactor operators might not have shut down the reactor until more serious damage had been done.

In short, the accident that happened was a bit worse than the "maximum credible accident," and the results worse than foreseen by its designers. More than one subassembly was damaged, the reactor did not shut down, and there was some release of radioactivity. It should be emphasized that the "maximum credible accident" was assumed to occur at a power level fifteen times that at which the actual accident occurred. In other words, the actual accident was not only "incredible," it might have been far worse.

Whether a disastrous accident like that described in the 1957 report could have happened remains a matter for speculation. Despite the confidence of its designers, the Fermi reactor is surrounded with a steel and concrete containment which is designed to withstand the force of an explosion of 600 pounds of TNT. The question of whether a core meltdown could produce an explosion greater than this, and whether the containment would in fact completely contain such an explosion, is the subject of a great deal of detailed calculation and educated guesswork. Since an experimental test of these calculations would require the destruction of at least one extremely expensive reactor, they are likely to remain unconfirmed unless and until a still more "incredible" accident happens.

Fermi, in any case, is out of commission for some time, and perhaps for good. But, at the same American Nuclear Society meeting in April of 1967 at which the Fermi accident was first described in detail,[12] four major American firms announced plans to build new prototype fast breeder reactors. General Electric, Westinghouse, Atomics International and General Dynamics Corporation all presented different designs; (Babcock and Wilcox have since made public their fast reactor plans); GE is farther down the road than the other firms, and intends to build sodium-cooled fast breeders, of the same general type as the Fermi reactor. The companies plan construction of prototypes roughly the size of Fermi's original design in two or three years, and aim toward commercial plants in the 1980's. These would be 1,000,000-kilowatt plants.

Plans for operating plants five times Fermi's size only fifteen years from now may seem a little precipitous (even a proved reactor type requires seven years from the time of the order to the manufacturer to the date of operation). Despite complaints of foot-dragging from industry, however, the AEC has accepted this schedule in rough outline. The official program for fast breeder development is at present being circulated for comment, and will appear late in 1968. The 1967 AEC report[13] to the President stated: "It does not appear that a prudent commitment to build the first U.S. demonstration plant can be made before 1969. . . ." Members of the Joint Congressional Committee on Atomic Energy seem to feel the program is not being pushed vigorously enough, however, and this position is apparently prompted by the same fear that spurs industry — the threat of foreign competition in the growing nuclear reactor market. In a guest editorial in *Nucleonics,* a trade journal, Craig Hosmer, ranking Republican House member of the Joint Committee on Atomic Energy asks:

"In the 1980's will U.S. utilities order fast breeder reactors from the U.K.?" He goes on to criticize severely the AEC's program in this field, and concludes, "Our fast breeder commercialization schedule must be telescoped to 1980 or earlier if the AEC is to serve the nation's nuclear needs on time and preserve our lead in nuclear technology." [14]

There is enormous pressure on the AEC from both industry and Congress to accelerate the fast breeder program. Several reactor manufacturers have already formed joint agreements with groups of private utilities (Detroit Edison, principal architect of the Fermi project, is prominent among these) to finance design and construction of prototypes, presumably with federal assistance. In 1968 or 1969, applications will probably be made to the AEC for construction permits and for funds.

This schedule has not been set back noticeably by the accident at Fermi, yet the fact that severity of the October 5 accident somewhat exceeded expectations diminishes confidence in the assurances of the safety of fast breeders given by reactor engineers and by the AEC. The potential economic benefits of breeders, and the threat of foreign competition, seem to outweigh the potential hazards, at least for the AEC and Joint Committee.

In a recent address Wilfred E. Johnson, a member of the AEC, commented on the economic benefits of fast reactors in terms of lowered electric bills. A saving of a tenth of a cent per kilowatt hour, Johnson said, "which seems entirely feasible, will by the year 2000, mean a saving to the public each year of four billion dollars." He estimated the cost of developing the program at two billion dollars, to be borne largely by the Federal Government.[15]

There is a large question mark in the economic equation, however, which perhaps accounts more than anything else for the AEC's present comparatively conservative policy on fast breeders. This is the question of reliability.

Commercial power plants are being built ever larger; the first commercial fast breeders will have a capacity of a million kilowatts of electricity or more, enough to supply a good-sized city. The construction of such large central plants is made possible by the increasing connectedness of power systems, which means that when power from a large plant is not needed locally (as for instance late at night) it can be shipped to far distant points. By the 1980's, perhaps all of this country and even most of the North American continent will be interconnected in a single huge power grid.

The failure of a very large generating plant and its removal from service for an extended period of time, however, could cause a severe and extended power shortage.

There is, therefore, an increasing emphasis on power plant reliability, and so far the sodium-cooled reactor has shown itself to be singularly unreliable. This stems largely from the difficulty of handling molten sodium at high temperatures — typically at about 1000°F. This material reacts explosively with air and water, and yet in a power plant, the heat from the sodium must somehow be transferred to water to produce the steam needed to run turbines which in turn drive the electric generators. The difficulty of achieving this feat has plagued Fermi and other plants like it. The reactor at Hallam, Nebraska, intended to improve sodium-cooling technology, has finally been abandoned, after years of difficulties. Hallam and Fermi were the only two sodium-cooled reactors to be placed in commercial power grids in this country, and both were out of operation during most of their lifetimes because of difficulties with the sodium systems.

Only time and expensive experimentation will tell whether these difficulties can be overcome. The Experimental Breeder Reactor II at Arco, Idaho, is the only remaining sodium-cooled fast reactor in this country; other test facilities are under construction or are being planned. Whether on industry's short schedule, or on the AEC's slightly longer one, this country seems firmly committed to a $2 billion fast breeder development program. In its 1967 report to the President, the AEC stated:

> Emphasis is being placed on the high gain breeders as recommended in the 1962 report. In particular, the program for development of the liquid metal-cooled [sodium] fast breeder has been substantially augmented. . . .[16]

. . . The sodium-cooled fast breeder choice is based on potential economies, industrial and worldwide interest, technological experience, and its capability to conserve uranium resources.[17]

. . . Plans are being developed for the introduction of a number of sodium-cooled fast breeder demonstration plants to be built during the 1970's.[18]

The AEC's fiscal 1968 budget includes $71,350,000 for development of fast breeder reactors.

The growing commitment to fast breeder reactors as "the next step" in the reactor program may be premature, as the real first step — commercial water-moderated plants — has not yet really been taken. The first of these which are expected to be commercially feasible (at San Onofre, California, and Nine Mile Point in New York) went into operation early in 1968. It will be some time before enough experience has been gained to judge whether or not their predicted economic advantages are to materialize. For most of the country, even more advanced (and larger) plants will be required to compete economically with coal-burning plants, and the first of these 800,- 000- to 1,000,000-kilowatt plants will not go into operation until around 1970. All reactors which are presently in operation are considered experimental, and are far from being economically competitive with conventional plants.

Fast breeders will, therefore, have to compete, not with current electric power plants, but with the 1,000,000-kilowatt plants of the future, and to do so, they will have to be at least as large. This fivefold increase over the size of the Fermi plant brings with it a similar increase in hazard. In an article which appeared in August, 1967, Dr. Edward Teller wrote:

In order for [a fast breeder reactor to] work economically in a sufficiently big power-producing unit, it probably needs quite a bit more than one ton of plutonium. I do not like the hazard involved. . . .

If you put together two tons of plutonium in a breeder, one-tenth of one percent of this material could become critical. . . .

In an accident involving a plutonium reactor, a couple of tons of plutonium can melt. I don't think anybody can foresee where 1 or 2 or 5 percent of this plutonium will find itself and how it will get mixed with some of the other material. A small fraction of the original charge can become a great hazard.[19]

When fast breeder reactors grow to the size which Dr. Teller discusses, a whole new class of hazards appears. Dr. Teller touched on these. Writing in 1964, Walter J. McCarthy, whom we have already met, and Dr. David Okrent, past chairman of the Advisory Committee on Reactor Safeguards, describe another possibility:

Under a number of circumstances, one part of a large reactor core may heat, even to the melting point, while other areas are relatively unaffected, as seems to have happened in the Fermi accident. As in that case, blockage of a liquid coolant nozzle might cause a temperature increase in one portion of the reactor so great that the fuel in that area would melt; local melting, in one portion of the core, could be followed by the collecting and refreezing of the fuel in a prompt critical configuration and a mild explosion equal perhaps to several hundred pounds of TNT, which could be contained by the reactor structures.

The possibility that only a portion of such a reactor melts, undergoes a relatively mild explosion which acts to compress other parts of the core extremely rapidly, thus instigating a very much larger energy release, needs further investigation.[20]

Compressing large amounts of fissionable material by means of an explosion is precisely what happens in an atomic bomb. This possibility does indeed seem to call for further study. A "very much larger energy release" could be a full-scale nuclear explosion.

WHY REACTORS?

SOMEDAY COAL, OIL AND NATURAL GAS will be in short supply. The amount of these fossil fuels present in the earth's crust is limited; our consumption of them increases at an ever-growing rate. At some point we must face the need to replace this source of energy on which all of industrial society depends. How soon will that time come?

> . . . we cannot long maintain our present rate of increase of [coal] consumption . . . the check to our progress must become perceptible within a century from the present time . . . the cost of fuel must rise, perhaps within a lifetime, to a rate injurious to our commercial and manufacturing supremacy. . . ." [1]

> . . . the United States may be able for the next few years (five or ten) to meet the increased demands for petroleum and . . . thereafter the production may remain stationary for another short period, following which there will be a period of twenty or more years during which production will decrease from year to year, while consumption increases, causing greater and greater imports from foreign fields and higher prices, culminating in acute shortage. [2]

> Reserves of such "low-cost" . . . fossil fuels are small by comparison with the maximum plausible demands. . . . new sources

of low-cost energy must begin to carry some of the load by A.D. 1975 or sooner, and much of it by A.D. 2000, if we are not to run the risk of seeing economic systems throughout the non-Communist world falter in the face of steeply rising costs of energy.[3]

The first of the quoted paragraphs was written in 1865, the second in 1916. The third quotation is from an Atomic Energy Commission study published in 1953. All three of these prophecies have proved incorrect. Prophecies of doom have a long history: the earliest scholarly warning that coal was about to be exhausted (that the author has been able to find) dates from the late eighteenth century. Yet coal prices at present are dropping, and current estimates are that they will remain stable or drop further for the rest of this century. Domestic United States oil is heavily protected from competition from foreign imports; natural gas sales continue to expand. Despite the many warnings of scarcity which we continue to hear, there seems to be an abundance of fossil fuel.

How much coal, oil and gas do we really have? Estimates vary widely and, oddly enough, seem to increase with time. In 1953, Palmer Putnam, acting as consultant to the AEC, estimated that the United States had reserves of fuel recoverable at "substantially present costs" of 4 Q. ("Q" is the usual unit for estimating such large quantities of fuel; it is a measure of the energy content of fuel equal to a quintillion British Thermal Units.) Putnam quotes another estimate made in 1952 by Ayres and Scarlott which gives the "minimum plausible ultimate" reserves of coal, oil and gas, in the United States, as "about 5.2 Q." These figures were alarming, for Putnam estimated that the United States economy would require at least 4.3 Q by the year 2000. Unless other sources of energy were found, all of the country's economical fuels would be exhausted in this century.[4]

By 1962, things looked a little brighter. Putnam had predicted: "peak production of oil-gas may be reached between 1955 and 1960.

"Peak production of good coking bituminous coal may be reached before 1960."

In 1962, ten years after those words were written, coal prices were still dropping, and coal, oil and gas production were all increasing. The Atomic Energy Commission issued its report to the President on civilian nuclear power, in which it summarized some more recent estimates of fuel reserves. These ranged from 26 Q (U.S. Geological Survey) to 130 Q (Department of the Interior).[5] The lower figure indicated that fuel resources would be exhausted in a hundred years; 130 Q, on the other hand, would not be exhausted for two centuries despite rapidly increasing rates of consumption.

Shortly after this report appeared, President Kennedy requested the heads of nine federal departments to undertake a comprehensive study of "the development and utilization of our total energy resources." A steering committee was formed, and it in turn established an Energy Study Group under the leadership of Dr. Ali Bulent Cambel. A year later this Group produced the exhaustive "Energy R&D and National Progress," the most thorough and authoritative examination of the nation's energy resources and prospects ever undertaken.[6]

Basing its recommendations on the detailed findings of the Cambel report, the Steering Committee issued its own report in 1966.[7] They estimated total United States fuel resources as between 1,040 and 1,064 Q.[8] Consumption was expected to rise to slightly less than one-seventh Q per year by the end of this century. At that rate, fuel resources in this country would be adequate for something over seven thousand years.

What accounts for the discrepancies among the various estimates of fuel resources? Putnam and other writers, even today, see the almost immediate exhaustion of our coal, oil and gas; the federal interdepartmental study shows resources adequate for thousands of years. Most of these authors, nevertheless, work with the same basic knowledge of geology and with the reported reserves of mining companies and their estimates of future discoveries.

The reason for the differences among estimates is simply a matter of fuel cost. In 1865, W. Stanley Jevons, M.A., L.L.D., F.R.S., first published *The Coal Question: An Inquiry Concerning the Progress of the Nation, and the Probable Exhaustion of our Coal-mines,* a book, quoted earlier, which has become a minor classic of economics. Mr. Jevons, who, among other honors held the Stanley Jevons Chair at Owens College, Manchester, feared not the actual exhaustion of coal, but its increasing price:

> It is shown that in all probability there is no precise physical limit of deep mining, but that the growing difficulties of management and extraction of coal in a very deep mine must greatly enhance its price. . . .
>
> Should the consumption multiply for rather more than a century at the same rate, the average depth of our coal-mines would be 4,000 feet, and the average price of coal much higher than the highest price now paid for the finest kinds of coal.
>
> It is thence simply inferred that we cannot long continue our present rate of progress.[9]

This is precisely the same argument made by Putnam one hundred years later, in his report to the AEC which has influ-

enced so much rhetoric about the need for atomic energy. Putnam made what are still reasonably accurate estimates of fuel
resources which were "recoverable substantially at present costs
by present methods." "Present" refers to 1950. The booby trap
here, as it was in Mr. Jevons' prophecies of doom a century before, is in the phrase "present methods." Jevons could not foresee the great advances in coal-mining technology which made
it possible to mine cheaply coal seams which were simply inaccessible to mid-nineteenth-century technology. Putnam sim-
ilarly writes off this country's huge reserves of oil shale (as
much as 1600 Q in the Cambel report), because in 1950 there
was no cheap way of mining this resource. "If we are to avoid
the risk of seriously increased real unit costs of energy in the
United States, then new low-cost sources should be ready to
pick up much of the load by 1975 or sooner." Putnam could
write these words in 1953 because the great advances in coal-
mining and transportation techniques which have brought coal
prices down over the last fifteen years were not yet making
themselves evident. If coal and oil costs had not remained low,
however, only a slight increase would have spurred the development of the oil shale mining technology, tapping the greatest
supply of fuel in this country or in the world.

Oil shale is a sedimentary rock whose polished surface is rem-
iniscent of mahogany. Trapped between the twin layers of the
rock is a hydrocarbon, kerogen, which can be converted to oil
plus a solid residue, coke, by heating; rich ores may be as much
as 65 percent hydrocarbon. The richest presently-known deposit is the Green River Shale, which extends over 16,000
square miles in Wyoming, Colorado and Utah. In order to release the oil, shale must be crushed and then heated; the liquid
released is petroleum much like that which comes from wells.

Present mining methods (oil shale is used in a few parts of the world, and a recent Canadian project is mining the similar Athabasca tar sands) involve digging the rock out of the ground, crushing it and then heating or "retorting" it to extract the oil. This is an expensive process, and furthermore produces huge quantities of crushed-rock waste which must somehow be disposed of. A potentially more promising method is "in situ retorting." This involves detonating explosives in the oil shale underground, accomplishing the crushing of a large volume of rock. A zone of controlled burning, regulated by compressed air, could be driven through the zone of fractured rock. The kerogen, heated by the advancing front, would decompose into oil and coke. The oil would drain to the bottom of the region of the crushed rock, and be pumped to the surface. The coke remaining in the rock would provide fuel to continue the retorting. This process would avoid the scarring of the landscape and the problem of disposing of the crushed-rock wastes, which remain underground.

The Department of the Interior has recently begun doing research on in situ retorting, and so has the Atomic Energy Commission. An explosion of a small nuclear weapon underground might release huge quantities of oil from shale. According to a recent news story, "One Atomic Energy Commission official has predicted that when this happens the [oil] companies will be able to produce oil from shale at a cost of only 29 cents per barrel. Crude oil now costs roughly $2.50 a barrel." [10]

To be sure, the oil produced in this way might be radioactive and therefore unusable or costly to use. Conventional explosives may provide more promise. No matter what the eventual process used, however, it is clear that oil shale represents a huge untapped reserve of potentially cheap fuel; the Green

River Shale alone is estimated to contain about 2 trillion bar-
rels of oil. Should other fuel become more expensive, this reserve will certainly be drawn upon.

It is easy to see, therefore, how Putnam and Cambel could
come to such differing conclusions using the same basic facts;
with only the then-available technology, Putnam was right in
saying that resources would soon be exhausted. Cambel and
the interdepartmental study group were more foresighted, and
reckoned up all the potential resources which might be tapped
in future, including low-grade oil shale at depths down to 20,-
000 feet.

Putnam perpetuates a venerable position, one which economist Harold Barnett calls the "myth of our vanishing resources."
The interdepartmental study group, on the other hand, may be
too optimistic. At some point short of total exhaustion, the energy required to extract fuels from the earth becomes as great
as the energy contained in them.

All we can say with any degree of certainty is that some time
in the future, probably centuries hence, we will be confronted
with a shortage of fuel, if industrial civilizations continue on
the course of the last two hundred years. Probably at some
point before that, fossil fuels will become more valuable as raw
materials for manufacturing synthetic chemicals than as fuel
(a change which is already being felt in the oil industry), and
our heat and power will be derived from other sources. If present economic and social patterns persist, then atomic energy
should certainly be examined as a possible replacement for coal,
oil and gas. Other alternatives, such as fusion and solar power,
should also be explored.

A prudent man would therefore likely recommend that in the
next century or two we try to develop an economical and safe

source of atomic power. There does not seem to be any urgency about this, however; the fuel shortage can hardly explain the present pace of the atomic energy program. What does account for the present rush to atomic power? The following are the principal stated justifications for nuclear reactors. With one exception, these all derive from the supposed cheapness or prospective cheapness of electric power generated by the atom.

The stated virtues of a program are not always identical with the personal motives of those who propound it. Although the program must be judged on explicit benefits and risks, these do not often give us any real idea of the reason for the program's existence, or of the circumstances which have created the need to make a judgment. Thus the shortages of fuels, uranium as well as coal, which seemed to face this country in the 1940's and which prompted so much of the early interest in fast breeder reactors, have now withdrawn into the distant future — yet the pace of the reactor program expands. On the other hand, many of the reasons now given for building reactors were simply not considered when the development of these plants was undertaken. To a certain extent, all enterprises have inertia and once set in motion tend to proceed, generating ever new justifications, even though their original purpose has long ago disappeared.

The magnitude and speed of the present reactor program indicate that much more than simple inertia is operating, however. In earlier chapters, we have tried to show two factors which have contributed to the present program. Both are consequences of military development of atomic energy. On the one hand, a number of large manufacturing firms made considerable investments of capital and talent in military-contract projects, investments on which they were reasonably anxious

to find new sources of return. On the other hand, civilian customers for reactors were created through the fears felt both by
private utilities and by members of the government, in both the
Congress and the Executive, regarding federal investment in
military reactors. It was felt that this was a step toward feder-
ally-owned civilian power plants, and advocates of privately
owned power wished to preempt the field. These two pressures, acting on the Atomic Energy Commission and the Congress, as well as more directly on manufacturers and utilities,
accounted, I believe, for much of the urgency of the effort to
develop economical atomic power, and are acting as strongly
now as they ever did.

A third, and more subtle, pressure was created by this country's investment in military nuclear programs. Particularly in
its early days, the atomic energy program was operated by ci-
vilians. To the thousands of scientists and engineers engaged
on the Manhattan Project, the development — and then the use
— of a major scientific discovery for simple destruction was re-
pugnant. The arms race which followed so quickly after the
war was also highly disturbing to many within and outside the
new Atomic Energy Commission. The thought of peaceful
blessings from the atom to counterbalance its destructiveness
gave a good deal of comfort to those whose responsibility was
the development of nuclear weapons. David Lilienthal, first
chairman of the Atomic Energy Commission, tells in his journal
of the pleasure which both he and President Truman felt at the
medical and research advances which radioactive isotopes
made possible.[11]

The wish that atomic energy not be simply an unmitigated
curse of weapons is felt by most of us in this country. It accounts in large part, I think, for the strenuous advocacy of reac-

tors by many who have participated in one way or another in military atomic development. It is a more creditable motive than the strictly economic arguments generally advanced by such advocates. Reactors must be judged on their merits, however, and aside from fuel conservation and one further exception, all the claims are economic.

The other exception is the argument that reactors avoid the serious air pollution problems created by plants which burn coal, oil or gas. This argument can be made only because we have not yet had to confront the problems which will be created by radioactive pollution of air, water and soil by reactors and their associated industry. Unfortunately, we have already experienced the enormous discomforts and damages of pollution from fossil fuel burning. There are always, it seems, many who are ready to exchange a present danger for one which is still securely in the future. Yet it does seem that, if the reactor program continues on the course it has begun, the problems of radioactive pollution, ten, twenty or more years ahead, will make present difficulties seem trivial. Our descendants may wonder how, in the face of past mistakes, we could go on to make such another terrible one.

It is not going to be possible to exchange one set of problems for another in any real way. By all estimates, most of the electric power in this country will be produced by fossil-fuel burning plants for some years to come. The Atomic Energy Commission estimates that the major portion of power will be generated by fossil plants until the year 2,000. With the steady growth of our population and the more rapid growth of power needs, this means that not only will present coal, oil, and gas consumption continue, but that it will increase drastically in the next thirty years. A coal industry source gives the estimate of 829 million tons of coal to be supplied to electric utilities in the year 2000 compared to 242 million tons sold in 1965.[12]

Nuclear power is, therefore, no cure for air pollution problems, even if it did not create a more serious problem of its own. Sanguine announcements by utilities that they are "going nuclear" to combat air pollution are simply ways of trying to avoid a problem which will not go away. Air pollution from coal, oil, and gas must be dealt with; reliance on atomic power is both dangerous and misleading.

These are not, however, the only factors weighed when a power company is deciding whether its next plant will be fired by coal or atomic energy. Dollars and cents must also have been important in deciding the rush to reactors of the past three years. For nuclear reactors do seem to be, at some times and places, the cheapest way to produce power. And their economy is due to the fact that, to an extent unprecedented in American history, their costs are passed on to the taxpayer and the general public.

The costs of reactors are passed on to the public in two ways: by avoiding the necessary steps to limit radioactive pollution, the nuclear industry allows the public to pay in health damages what the industry should be preventing with dollars; by hiding behind the protection of the Price-Anderson Act, the nuclear industry is avoiding the cost of necessary safety measures and passing it on to the taxpayer and the general public, who provide the insurance for and suffer the physical risk of nuclear power plants.

In Chapter IV we saw that neither power companies nor reactor manufacturers would be interested in atomic electricity if it were not for the Price-Anderson Act, which excuses them from assuming the responsibility for the risk inherent in their industry. The federal insurance provided under this act makes nuclear power economically attractive; without that support and subsidy it would not be. What has happened is that the Federal Government, largely through the prodding of the Joint Committee on Atomic Energy, has exempted nuclear power from the normal competitive restraints of the marketplace. Freed from economic restraint, it has grown at a pace which endangers us all.

Used properly, atomic energy might be a valuable force in the civilian as well as the military economy. Reactors can be safe and clean; further research might make them so, at a price which would still allow their use in a competitive economy. The passage of Price-Anderson has removed the incentive to do the needed research, however, and instead we are developing, not safer, but more dangerous reactors, the fast breeders discussed in the last chapter, the hazards of which make even the present plans for huge reactors in the hearts of cities seem tame.

One of the ways in which reactors might be made more safe would obviously be to put them in unpopulated areas. Recent advances in transmitting electric power long distances over extra high voltage (EHV) transmission lines allow a plant to be quite far from its customers; with EHV transmission, a reactor could be hundreds of miles from any city. This would, of course, increase the cost of nuclear power, but further advances in transmission technology will probably reduce the penalty. A more serious difficulty is the requirement for large amounts of cooling water for reactors; sites with the needed water which are also sufficiently isolated are rare, and becoming more scarce each year.

There are a number of conceivable ways out of this impasse. We might restrict reactors to only the few remote locations suitable; we might develop reactors which are economical, and yet small enough to be housed in an impenetrable containment; or new reactor designs which did not require so much — or any — cooling water could be developed. The latter two possibilities have received some attention, but research on new reactor types has all but halted in this country, with the exception of fast breeder development.

Small reactors are attractive for a number of reasons, the greatest being that containing the radioactivity released in an accident becomes possible with small reactors. Under 100,000 kilowatts is a size we have some experience with, and as indicated earlier, it seems possible to enclose them in a "thermos-bottle" containment which will not be breached in an accident — although again possibility is not certainty. Such small plants would be highly attractive to the many small rural cooperative and municipal electric power companies which are themselves too small to invest in the mammoth reactors which are now being marketed.

The whole trend of the country's economy and technology is away from small power plants and toward ever-larger ones in increasingly interconnected power systems; the economic incentives for small plants seem small. And, too, distributing many small reactors over the landscape increases the chance of small accidents, negligence and the increasing load of accidental radioactive release during transportation of wastes. Another difficulty with the small plant is that the pollution controls which will be increasingly needed for reactor operation will probably not be much cheaper for a small plant than for a larger one, putting a very heavy burden on the former.

A large reactor, which requires little or no cooling water, and which is in a remote location with its own waste-disposal system, seems a distinct possibility, and by far the most attractive one. All that would go into such a plant would be relatively innocuous uranium fuel; all that would come out would be electricity. The reactor and waste-disposal systems would be designed to prevent emissions of radioactivity; the wastes of irradiated fuel would be buried in impermeable formations deep underground. Such a completely self-contained reactor installation could be in desert or mountainous country, tied into the nation's power grid through EHV transmission lines. Far from any center of population, even an accident disastrous to the reactor itself would not be a disaster to any nearby city. Underground construction may be an important safety device. It is already in use in Sweden.

There is no reason, in principle, why such a remote, underground, self-contained large reactor cannot be developed to the point where it is competitive with other forms of power generation. There are a number of ways in which large power stations could economically do away with most of their requirements for cooling water; cooling towers and ponds are already in use in areas where heat poses a hazard to water quality or to fishing. Commonwealth Associates, nuclear consultants, have recently proposed an economically competitive design for use in Iowa which would rely on well water.[13]

A more difficult task would be removing all the radioactive waste releases from the reactor and fuel-processing cycle. One step toward this goal could be made quite easily, however, and that is to avoid all transportation losses by locating the plant for processing spent nuclear fuel on the same site as the reactor, and by burying the wastes extracted from the spent fuel at the same location. This is already feasible for large plants — in fact, is already being done with one government-owned reactor, Experimental Breeder Reactor II. If the reactor fuel were also manufactured at the reactor, as it is at the EBR-II site, then all the hazards of transporting radioactive materials would be wiped out. Only unirradiated and therefore relatively harmless uranium (unused fuel can be safely held in the hand) would be shipped to the plant; nothing would be shipped out except electricity. In 1966, Cyril M. Slansky of the Phillips Petroleum Company, Atomic Energy Division, presented a paper before an AEC waste-disposal symposium which showed that at least for some kinds of reactors and fuels, such a completely self-contained system would be as cheap as the present method, which involves the expensive and hazardous transportation of nuclear wastes from the reactor to a distant processing plant.[14]

The principal objection to this scheme raised at the symposium was the fact that present regulations require wastes to be buried on government-owned land. The requirement stems from the extremely long times, ranging into centuries, that the waste will remain dangerous. It is felt that only on government-owned land is continuity of surveillance properly assured. This would not be an insurmountable problem if reactors were restricted to remote locations, for there are probably many such sites on government-owned land. Alternatively, provisions might be made to have ownership of a reactor site pass to the Federal Government in case its private owner is unwilling or unable to continue management.

A more difficult problem would be that of reducing and eventually eliminating the radioactive pollutants released by reactors and fuel-reprocessing plants. The problem is clearly soluble, however. Reactors, even in their current form, could be operated so that, with few exceptions, no pollutants would be released. For it should be remembered that even when the fuel elements are leaking, the radioactive wastes can be retained within the coolant water (at least in pressurized water reactors). All present releases from reactors are intentional, in the sense that the released contaminants could be retained and packaged for burial like the more highly concentrated wastes from the fuel. All that is required is the extra expense of retaining and concentrating the lower-level wastes.

One exception is the noble gas produced in reactor fuel. Noble gases, especially krypton and xenon, are extremely difficult to capture, partly because they are gases, and partly because they do not enter into chemical reactions very easily (hence, the appellation "noble"). Although laboratory methods for trapping these gases into solid compounds are available, commercial-scale techniques have not been developed. There is no reason in principle why this could not be done.

Another exception is tritium (radioactive hydrogen), which physically becomes a part of the cooling water. This is a serious problem even now, and will not be easily solved.

In principle, then, it is possible to end all intentional releases of radioactivity to the environment. Accidental releases would be much reduced by housing all the elements of fuel fabrication and processing at the reactor site. Disposal of radioactive wastes by dumping them in rivers or in the ocean, or by releasing them into the air, or by burying them in shallow graves near the surface could be entirely ended simply by concentrating all wastes, reducing them to solid form or packing them into unbreakable containers, and burying them deep underground in salt caves or granite formations which would not be disturbed for thousands of years.

Although present reactors could, at least in principle, be made safe and clean, it is hard to see how the far greater difficulties of the fast breeder are to be solved. Yet, fast breeders are being justified in exactly the same terms that water-cooled reactors have been justified. We *must* have them, because uranium is in short supply. Soon it will start going up in price, and the reactors we have built will become ever more expensive to operate, until the irreplaceable uranium is all exhausted. Breeder reactors, which make more fuel than they burn, are an inexhaustible energy source.

It is not likely that this argument will prove to be true of uranium, where it has proved false of coal and oil. Uranium is a plentiful element. The present seeming shortage is caused by lack of demand for uranium in recent years; very little prospecting has been done since the AEC stopped enlarging its military requirements for the metal. Since the reactor boom began to take hold, prospecting has revived, and it seems almost certain that vast new reserves will soon be uncovered.

Even if this should not be so, however, low-grade ores are already known which are more than adequate for our energy needs for quite some time to come. The Cambel report points out that even if all the electric power in this country were to be generated by nuclear fuel, which is very far from being the case, there is sufficient uranium for many years. The interdepartmental study group concludes, "All the estimates indicate that *either* coal or uranium resources *alone* are adequate to take us through the year 2000 and longer."

In the August 1967 issue of *Nuclear News,* Dr. Edward Teller said, "There probably is enough uranium, and breeders will not be needed in the foreseeable future, such as a hundred years or 300 years, or longer. . . . I wonder, if we were to resume the needed research in mining and chemical engineering to obtain improved methods of uranium extraction, how greatly we would then increase our uranium reserves."

As in the past, the principal virtues claimed for fast breeder reactors, as for their predecessors, will be economic. What reactors really represent is a choice between higher electric bills and greater risk to life and health. The public bears the full costs in either case.

In all this we are rather charitably assuming that reactors would, in fact, produce cheaper power. This is simply an assumption, for none of the reactors which presumably will do this have yet been built. The costs of reactor power are estimated on the basis of information provided by their manufacturers. In many cases the estimates may be less than reliable. In his authoritative study of the atomic energy program, *Contracting for Atoms*, Harold Orlans discusses the calculations, down to several decimal places, of projected costs of atomic power and notes. "Some of the assumptions upon which these calculations are based are so gross, the decimal places are 'a joke in the fraternity,' one reader observes." [15] Baltimore Gas and Electric recently *opposed* a reduction in its rates in part because of "the company's plans to expand in the nuclear field." [16]

Somewhere along the line, in any case, a decision has been made that the benefits of nuclear reactors outweigh their hazard. It is difficult to see just where this determination was made (if indeed such decisions are made at a single time and place). One point at which it could at least have been challenged was that at which the Price-Anderson Act was proposed.

For here was a straightforward statement of the judgment: The benefits of the reactor program, as it presently exists, are great enough for the public, through the Federal Government, to assume its risks.

There was little debate of this bill in Congress, in the newspapers or elsewhere in the country outside the nuclear establishment itself. Except for the opposition of insurance companies and among parties to the debate over the Fermi reactor, the bill, like the reactor program as a whole, passed almost unchallenged. This was all the more surprising for, aside from the enormous potential dangers of the reactor program, the bill empowered the Federal Government to intervene in private industry to an unprecedented extent.

Why has there been, and why does there continue to be, such nearly complete lack of criticism of the Price-Anderson Act and of the nuclear power program as a whole? Although there has been sporadic opposition to nuclear plants from their prospective neighbors, and general concern has been growing, both remain to a large degree helpless or inarticulate. This helplessness derives from two sources, both of which are common to many modern technological enterprises which affect the public at large.

First, the question of reactor safety and usefulness involves a number of extremely complex and difficult scientific questions. Most people who are not professionally engaged in the nuclear field tend to feel that these questions are beyond their grasp. Believing themselves incapable of forming an independent judgment, many feel that the government experts must know what they're doing. Yet, more and more, we are beginning to find that the attitude of "leave it to the experts" often produces unwelcome results. A growing proportion of the national resources and manpower are being devoted to large technological projects, like the space program and the construction of a supersonic transport, which few of us understand. The benefits and dangers of these programs are not always clear; yet, if only through our tax bill, they affect us all.

It was only with the publication of *Silent Spring* that the public at large discovered they were being exposed to potentially grave hazards from the use of pesticides. It was only after years of testing of nuclear weapons that many of us discovered the real hazards of radioactive fallout.

It was not until billions of pounds of detergents were disseminated in our water supplies that we discovered the nuisance and the pollution hazard this would pose. This relatively minor problem exemplifies the pattern of modern uses of science and technology. The drawbacks to a particular program never seem to be discovered until too late.

In the case of the reactor program, we are in a position to anticipate many of the difficulties which will soon be encountered. Warnings of what is to come have been seen at Bodega, at Humboldt Bay, at Fermi and elsewhere. It is long past time for a broader understanding of the risk from accident and radioactive pollution that present reactors pose, and the far greater risks of the fast breeder reactor which we are about to assume. The relevant information must be made available, and debate within Congress and outside it must begin. Only a very much broadened base of discussion will allow us to judge wisely whether in the reactor program, as it now stands, the benefits outweigh the hazards; only such a national discussion will enable us to judge among the various alternative ways of generating cheap and safe electrical power in the future.

Which brings us to the second reason that critics of the

reactor program have found themselves helpless. Modern science is profoundly affecting our political and legal system; traditional governmental organizations have not been adequate, and new forms, like the Joint Committee on Atomic Energy, and the Atomic Energy Commission, are appearing.

In *The Government of the Atom,* a study sponsored by the National Law Center, Harold Green and Alan Rosenthal say:

> The Joint Committee on Atomic Energy (JCAE), since its creation in 1946, has played an unusually influential role in the conduct of the nation's atomic enterprise. Although originally a part of the legislature, the Joint Committee's behavior uniquely resembles that of the higher echelons of the executive branch. In this respect, the JCAE represents a significant innovation in a governmental system of separated powers.
>
> Members of the Committee itself, other congressmen, and officials of the executive branch have long recognized the JCAE as an extraordinary Congressional institution. Despite its unique structure as the only joint committee with legislative powers, its broad statutory authority, and its unprecedented role in the formulation of national policy, the Committee has largely escaped the attention of scholars.[17]

We might add, and the attention of the general public, for surprisingly few have any real knowledge of the most powerful Congressional institution ever established, a major force in national policy formation over a wide range of foreign, domestic and military matters.

No less remarkable is the Atomic Energy Commission, the agency which has sole responsibility for the development and use of atomic energy. The AEC is also the agency with sole responsibility for regulation in this field. In fact, it is responsible for regulating its own activities, a situation which has been strongly criticized by its first chairman, David Lilienthal, among others.

The AEC has broader powers than have ever been given to a single federal agency. Among other things, the Atomic Energy Act of 1954 apparently gives the AEC power (according to its own contention) to impose security restrictions on any activities, whether conducted with or without government support, which bear on atomic energy, however tangentially. Regulations proposed by the AEC at the time of this writing, but not yet enacted, would allow the AEC to prohibit any research, whether undertaken by private individuals, private companies, universities or anyone else, which the AEC felt impinged on certain sensitive areas. The AEC has made clear its intention to broaden the areas coming under such control at any time it deems such action in the interest of national security or defense.

With sole authority in its area of activity, extremely broad powers, and with much of its activity cloaked by security restrictions on information, the AEC is a singularly difficult body to influence. It is subject only to the restraints of the Joint Committee, designated by law its "watchdog." Yet over the years, the two bodies have drawn together until they are almost indistinguishable. There has been considerable exchange of staff between the two bodies. The former Executive Director of the Joint Committee is now one of the five Commissioners who head the AEC, and, according to most observers, the most influential of the five. Although the senior members of the Joint Committee have been active in atomic energy affairs for twenty years or more, the Commissioners generally change with each Administration or, in most cases, even more frequently. Some remain on the Commission for only a single year. As a result, the Joint Committee dominates the AEC; at least in terms of the civilian reactor program, the two bodies have become one.

To compound this concentration of power, most scientists and engineers with experience of atomic energy are directly associated with the AEC or its contractors, or have received their training through the AEC. It is therefore not surprising that hearings before the Joint Committee show such little basic disagreement among expert witnesses, or that it is so difficult to contest the expert judgments produced by industry, the Joint Committee or the AEC.

In short, decision making in atomic energy programs has largely been removed from the normal process of open debate. There is no question but that the Joint Committee and the AEC are conscientious and acutely aware of the need for safety. Yet it is too much to ask them to make decisions unassisted which have such sweeping importance for society. It is too much to ask them to judge the safety and advisability of programs in the development of which they have themselves invested many years and great efforts.

IX

INFORMATION AND ACTION

FROM THE PRECEDING CHAPTER it will be seen that altering the
present course of atomic energy development in this country
would be no easy task. There are many billions of dollars invested or committed to present plans. The process of decision-
making is thoroughly insulated from outside criticism and
debate.

Yet we can see that many substantial improvements can be
made in the reactor program, without abandoning its present
basis. Reactors currently being manufactured are capable of
being modified for suitability at remote locations and for self-
contained operation. It may be too late to reconsider the national decision to invest in the development of atomic power,
but it is certainly not too late to decide how that investment
may best be used for the benefit of the nation's welfare and
health.

In the preceding chapters we have suggested some of the
reasons for the present shape of the reactor program. Whatever its history, that program is now clearly aimed toward the
accomplishment of narrow economic objectives, at a cost of
safety and pollution hazards which seems steep. The various
alternative routes to atomic power — and the even larger number of alternative means to reach cheaper electricity in general

— are not being considered. The single reason this state of affairs is permitted is simple. The public does not know about the risks the present course runs, nor that there are alternative actions, each with its own sets of benefits and risks, which might be considered.

This is a state of affairs which often holds true in social and political issues which derive from, or depend on, technology. These issues are effectively screened from outside examination by the public's — and in most cases, the Congress's — lack of facts. Whether it is an antiballistic missile system, or whether it is the nuclear power program, the supersonic transport, or a pointless race to the moon, we have been given not information, but judgments propounded by experts.

This is not a necessary state of affairs. In most cases, the pertinent facts can be made clear to a layman. This book is an attempt to demonstrate that belief. A far more important demonstration has been carried on for ten years by the Committee for Environmental Information, in St. Louis, Missouri.

In the middle 1950's, the American public became aware that their government was conducting a vast experiment, the testing of nuclear weapons, and that the results of that experiment had not been entirely foreseen. Beginning in 1954, the AEC began lifting the cover of secrecy from the fallout question, and a heated debate began. Official government statements, and scientists working in the weapon program, assured the public over and over that there was no hazard to health; many outside the government, and some within, were not so sure. But in fact, no one within or without the government really knew. The testing program had begun, and continued, in almost complete ignorance of the biological hazard from fallout. Violent disputes broke out among scientists, each proclaiming from the authority of his position his own opinion.

The public was naturally confused. When scientists of equal prominence took diametrically opposed stands, most people felt unable to resolve the dispute in their own minds. Not in possession of the basic facts himself, the layman could not choose among differing opinions.

The difficulty was acutely felt in St. Louis, which was a high-fallout area during most of the period of weapon testing. Radioactive strontium in St. Louis milk reached record highs. Government pronouncements assured that the levels were harmless — yet they continued to creep upward. Scientists from St. Louis universities were increasingly called upon to render their own judgments; doctors, especially pediatricians, were increasingly asked, "What should we do about the milk?" Dr. Barry Commoner, a St. Louis biologist, recalls being called upon to explain over and over again that the white spots on the lawn were mold, and not fallout.

Responding to the increasing demands for facts about fallout, St. Louis scientists and physicians joined with a group of concerned laymen to form the Committee for Nuclear Information. Although the founders of this group held varying moral and political judgments of the merits of bomb testing, the purpose of CNI was simply to provide the scientific evidence regarding the effects of fallout, to the extent that it was available. Where no real evidence existed, the group said so.

One of the founders of CNI described its early days this way: "About 200 people joined the group as soon as it was organized (about 30 being physicians and scientists) and contributed sufficient funds to permit a start. The technical members agreed to fill speaking engagements on nuclear problems, and in August 1958 a form letter offering this service was sent out to about 1,000 St. Louis civic organizations." Between October 1958 and December 1960, the group filled about 160 engagements. "The audiences [were] quite varied; about 50 church groups, about 45 PTA's and other school groups, about 30 fraternal, civic and professional organizations, and the remainder medical and scientific associations. A total estimated audience of 15–20,000 people [were] reached in this way." [1]

From its earliest days, CNI began publishing a monthly bulletin, *Nuclear Information*; in the ten years since its first issue, this has grown from four mimeographed pages to a national magazine with a professional staff. Although the CNI Speakers Bureau continues, the group's various publications have become its principal means of reaching a greatly enlarged audience. The first step toward this new role was taken in September of 1959, with the publication of "Nuclear War in St. Louis."

In May, 1959, the Joint Committee on Atomic Energy held extensive hearings to ascertain the extent of our knowledge of what might be the effects of a nuclear attack on the United States. Days of highly technical testimony were taken, detailed reports were submitted for the record. CNI arranged with the Joint Committee to obtain copies of the testimony as it was delivered; a team consisting of two physicists, two biologists and a physician prepared summaries of the physical, ecological and medical effects of the two nuclear bombs that the Joint Committee's assumed attack had assigned to St. Louis. A biologist who was also a talented writer, Dr. Florence Moog, translated these summaries into a fictional account of the supposed survivors of the hypothetical bombing of St. Louis.

The result was an accurate and moving account of what was known about nuclear warfare, and reached far more members of the public than the technical hearings on which it was based. "Nuclear War in St. Louis" was reprinted in 16 newspapers and magazines in six countries. CNI answered requests for 50,000 reprints of the publication, from church groups, schools, labor organizations; 2500 copies were ordered by state and federal civil defense organizations. Permission was granted to the War College, Air University of the United States Air Force, to reprint the bulletin for the use, within the War College, of each graduating class.

This was the first of a series of successes which were to confirm the judgment on which CNI was founded, that the public wanted, and could handle, the technical facts underlying political issues. In 1961, CNI published an analysis of the AEC's proposed Project Chariot, a plan to blast a harbor in the northern Alaskan shoreline, using nuclear explosives. The CNI article showed the peculiar biological risks from fallout in the region. In 1963, a detailed analysis of the difficulties involved in the planned reactor for Bodega Head in California was published.

In both cases, the CNI magazine reached large numbers of those most directly affected by the project; in Alaska, these were the inhabitants of scattered Eskimo villages along the coast, who have no written language of their own. The CNI bulletin, recorded on tape, "literally swept the Arctic coast, from Kakhtovik all the way down to Nome and below . . . ," according to one report. Both in California and in Alaska, it was the pressure of an informed citizenry which led eventually to abandonment of both projects; CNI was a large factor in providing the needed facts.

By 1964, it had become clear that the uses of atomic energy were only a few of the many political issues born from scientific progress. More and more large technological enterprises were making their effects felt in the environment, through growing pollution of air, water and soil, through the assaults of sonic booms and through the rapid degradation of the quality of life. Realizing that its experience in bringing information on atomic energy to the public would be invaluable in the wider range of science-based issues, CNI slowly began enlarging its scope, until in 1967 it formally became the Committee for Environmental Information; its monthly magazine is now *Scientist and Citizen.*

At about the same time, similar groups began appearing in other cities; the oldest of these is the Scientists' Committee for Public Information, in New York City. Similar groups in Washington, D.C., Denver, Colorado, Berkeley, California, Rochester, New York, Missoula, Montana, Minneapolis, Minnesota, and elsewhere began to form. A national coordinating body, the Scientists' Institute for Public Information, serves as a central organizing body for the dozen or so groups now active across the country. *Scientist and Citizen* has become the publication of this growing national "information movement."

The growing success of this movement gives considerable hope that the barrier between the atomic energy program and the general public is being breached, and that more than one voice will be heard when atomic energy is talked of; that the moral and political decisions regarding reactors will be made, at least in part, by those who will bear the consequences of the decisions. In short, we can hope that advancing science has not left democracy behind.

NOTES

INDEX

NOTES

The abbreviations AEC and JCAE used throughout represent the United States Atomic Energy Commission and the Joint Committee on Atomic Energy of the United States Congress, respectively. The abbreviation "WASH-740" represents a study done by the AEC entitled, "Theoretical Possibilities and Consequences of Major Accidents in Large Nuclear Power Plants."

CHAPTER I

1. The account of the accident at the NRX reactor is drawn principally from Lewis, W. B., "Accident to the NRX Reactor on December 12, 1952," Canadian Report AECL-232, Atomic Energy of Canada, Ltd. 1953, quoted in *The Technology of Reactor Safety*, Vol. 1, "Reactor Physics and Control," T. J. Thompson and J. G. Beckerley, eds. (Cambridge, M.I.T. Press, 1964), pp. 619–622.
2. The account of the Windscale Accident is drawn in part from "Accident of Windscale No. 1 Pile on 10th October, 1957," British Report Cmnd. 302 (London, November 1957), quoted in *The Technology of Reactor Safety*, pp. 633–635.
3. McCullough, C. Rogers, AEC, "The Windscale Accident," in *Proceedings*, 1958 AEC and Contractor Safety and Fire Protection Conference, June 24–25, 1958, TID-7591 AEC Technical Information Service, Oak Ridge, May 15, 1959, p. 76.
4. *Ibid.*, p. 78.
5. Thompson, T. J., in *The Technology of Reactor Safety*, Vol. 1, p. 699.

CHAPTER II

1. Quoted in Samuel Glasstone, *Sourcebook on Atomic Energy*, Second Edition (Princeton, D. Van Nostrand Co., Inc., 1958), p. 387.

2. Hahn, Otto, *New Atoms* (New York, Elsevier Publishing Co., Inc., 1950).
3. Quoted by Glasstone, *op. cit.*, p. 386.
4. Laurence, William, *Men and Atoms* (New York, Simon and Schuster, 1959).
5. *Ibid.*
6. Compton, Arthur Holly, *Atomic Quest* (New York, Oxford University Press, 1956).
7. Mullenbach, Philip, *Civilian Nuclear Power* (New York, the Twentieth Century Fund, 1963), p. 140.

CHAPTER III

1. San Francisco *Chronicle*, October 30, 1964.
2. Santa Rosa *Press Democrat*, March 19, 1963, p. 7.
3. Teller, Edward, "Energy From Oil and From the Nucleus," *Journal of Petroleum Technology*, May 1965, p. 506.
4. Saint-Amand, Pierre, "Geologic and Seismologic Study of Bodega Head," Northern California Association to Preserve Bodega Head and Harbor, 1963, p. 19.
5. Schlocker, Julius, and Manuel Bonilla, U.S. Department of the Interior, Geological Survey, "Engineering Geology of the Proposed Nuclear Power Plant Site on Bodega Head, Sonoma County, California," TEI-884, December 1963.
6. "Earthquakes, the Atom, and Bodega Head," Northern California Association to Preserve Bodega Head and Harbor, Berkeley, 1964.
7. *Ibid.*, p. 15.
8. *Ibid.*
9. *Ibid.*, p. 18.
10. Mattison, Lindsay, and Richard Daly, "Bodega, The Reactor, The Site, The Hazard," *Nuclear Information*, April 1964, available from the Committee for Environmental Information, 438 N. Skinker Blvd., St. Louis, Mo.
11. *Ibid.*
12. "The Proposed Malibu Nuclear Power Station," undated.
13. "Geology of Malibu Coastal Belt in Vicinity of Proposed Nuclear Reactor Site in Corral Canyon," Ventura, California, February 12, 1964, p. 7.

14. Quoted by Frank A. Morgan, Consulting Geologist, in "Review of Geological Work at the Proposed Corral Canyon Nuclear Reactor Site, Malibu," Los Angeles, January 21, 1965 (mimeographed), p. 2.
15. *Ibid.*
16. *Ibid.*, p. 3.
17. *Ibid.*
18. *Nucleonics Week,* April 30, 1967.
19. "An Assessment of Large Nuclear Powered Sea Water Distillation Plants," a Report of an Interagency Task Group, March, 1964, Office of Science and Technology, Executive Office of the President, TID-19267 UNC (revised).
20. Wyant, William K., Jr., "Proposed California Desalinization Plant," St. Louis *Post-Dispatch,* September 11, 1966.
21. *Nucleonics,* December 1966.
22. *Ibid.*
23. *Ibid.*
24. "The Ravenswood Reactor — a Preliminary Report to the Public," Citizens' Committee for Radiation Information, New York, undated (mimeographed).
25. March 21, 1963.

CHAPTER IV

1. "WASH-740," p. vii.
2. *Ibid.*, p. viii.
3. "Proposed Extension of AEC Indemnity Legislation," *Hearings,* Subcommittee on Legislation, JCAE, June 22–24, 1965, p. 348.
4. Commissioner John G. Palfrey, at a meeting of the Atomic Industrial Forum, quoted by David Pesonen in *The Nation,* October 18, 1965. Palfrey reportedly opened his talk by saying, "My assignment today was to review with you the updating of the Brookhaven report [WASH-740] . . . . Well, the Brookhaven study is not ready yet. . . . my guesses on what it will say or should say would be irresponsible chatter on a ticklish subject. . . ."
5. WASH-740, p. 3.
6. See "Nuclear Reactors Built, Being Built, or Planned," Appendix, TID-8200, revised annually by the Office of the Assistant General Manager for Reactors, AEC. The only reactors with which there had been extensive experience at the time of the report aside from

small experiments, were the military plutonium production reactors. The reliability of these is unknown, as details of their operations are classified.

7. WASH-740, p. 5.
8. Strauss, Lewis L., *Men and Decisions* (New York, Popular Library Inc., 1963).
9. Groves, Leslie R., Lt. Gen. USA Ret. *Now It Can Be Told* (New York, Harper and Bros., 1962).
10. Subcommittee on Legislation, JCAE, *Selected Materials on Atomic Energy Indemnity Legislation* (June 1965), p. 96.
11. Yount, Hubert W., Vice President, Liberty Mutual Insurance Co., appearing on behalf of the American Mutual Alliance, *Hearings*, on Governmental Indemnity before the JCAE, 84th Congress, second session, pp. 248–250.
12. *Selected Materials*, p. 66.
13. "Proposed Extensions of AEC Indemnity Legislation" *Hearings*, Subcommittee on Legislation, JCAE, June 22–24, 1965, p. 192.
14. *Ibid.*, p. 46.
15. Quoted by David Pesonen in *The Nation*, October 18, 1965.
16. Quad-Cities Station, Unit 1, Plant Design Analysis, Vol. I, Commonwealth Edison Company, Chicago, Illinois, p. V–1–20.
17. *Ibid.*, p. V–1–16.
18. *Nucleonics Week*, July 20, 1967, p. 3.
19. AEC Docket Number 50 — 259 & 260: letter dated March 14, 1967, from N. J. Palladino, Chairman ACRS to Honorable Glenn T. Seaborg, Chairman, AEC.
20. *Ibid.*
21. "Emergency Core Cooling: Report of Advisory Task Force on Power Reactor Emergency Cooling," AEC Division of Technical Information, Oak Ridge (undated), p. 6.
22. *Nucleonics*, June, 1967, p. 6.
23. Crawford, W. Donham, Remarks before Health Physics Society, Twelfth Annual Meeting, Washington, D.C., June 20, 1967 (mimeographed).
24. "Licensing and Regulation of Nuclear Reactors," *Hearings*, JCAE, April 4, 5, 6, and 20, and May 3, 1967, p. 129.
25. Hanchett, James, "Letter from Washington," *Nucleonics*, May, 1967, p. 11.
26. *Nucleonics Week*, June 15, 1967.

CHAPTER V

1. Slansky, Cyril M., "Waste Management in Close-Coupled Nuclear Fuel Cycles," *Proceedings*, Symposium on the Solidification and Long-Term Storage of Highly Radioactive Wastes, February 1966, CONF-660208, AEC, Oak Ridge. Slansky gives equilibrium values for a 1,000,000-kilowatt (electrical) reactor on a 1-year fuel cycle as 13,500 megacuries, including about 760 megacuries of cesium. Roughly 140 megacuries of cesium were released by the 140 megatons exploded through 1963. Other radionuclides are presumably in similar proportion. (See Federal Radiation Council Report 4, 1963).

2. Calder, Ritchie, *Living With the Atom* (Chicago, University of Chicago Press, 1962), p. 31.

3. Data from *Health Physics* 9:83 (1963) and 10:243 (1964), quoted in *Scientist and Citizen*, November, 1965, p. 8.

4. *Ibid.*

5. Calder, *op. cit.*, p. 37.

6. Commoner, Barry, *Science and Survival* (New York, Viking Press, 1966), p. 17.

7. Palmer, H. E., W. C. Hanson, B. I. Griffin, L. A. Braby, *Science*, Vol. 147 (1965), p. 620. See also Letters, *ibid.*, p. 1598.

8. Calder, *op. cit.*, p. 215.

9. Olson, J. S. and S. I. Auerbach, "Biological Contamination of Vegetation and Dispersal of Radioactive Wastes by Insects," *Nuclear Safety*, Vol. I, No. 3, p. 62.

10. This is a somewhat simplified account. Cellular mutations may appear as the result of errors in the repair of damage done to DNA rather than as a result of the damage itself, and it is quite possible that the damage is mediated by other substances and need not require a direct "hit" on a DNA molecule.

11. Blumenthal, Herman T., "Radiation and Aging," *Scientist and Citizen*, February 1957, p. 21.

12. *Ibid.*

CHAPTER VI

1. Engdahl, Don, in Santa Rosa *Press Democrat*, May 1, 1966.

2. Letter from Hal Stroube, Coordinator of Atomic Information to Hon. Mervyn M. Dymally, Chairman of the California State Assembly Committee on Industrial Relations, dated September 29, 1966, enclosing comments on the testimony of David Pesonen before the Committee.

3. *Ibid.*

4. Report to the AEC on operations during the period February to August, 1965, quoted by Don Engdahl in personal communication to author, dated May 26, 1966.

5. Stroube letter, *op. cit.*

6. In "Proposed Change No. 20" to the Humboldt operating license.

7. Stroube letter, *op. cit.*

8. Goodman, Leo, "Radiation Hazard in Modern Industry," Address to the American Public Health Association and the D.C. Public Health Association, April 26, 1967, Washington, D.C. (mimeographed), p. 4.

9. Coleman, J. R. and R. Liberace, *Radiological Health Data and Reports,* November 1966. They estimate exposures to the general population from reactor-produced krypton 85 dissolved in body fluids, at 20 to 100 millirads per year by the year 2060. Natural background radiation averages about 150 millirads; the NCRP guideline for exposure to the general population, from *all sources* is 170 millirads per year.

10. AEC Authorizing Legislation — 1968, *Hearings,* JCAE, March 14 and 15, 1967, Part 2, p. 883.

11. *Ibid.,* pp. 882–883.

12. *Ibid.*

13. *Civilian Nuclear Power: A Report to the President,* AEC Division of Technical Information, Oak Ridge, 1962, p. 4.

14. Goodman, Leo, *op. cit.,* p. 12.

15. *Proceedings,* First United Nations Conference on Peaceful Uses of Atomic Energy, Geneva, 1955, Vol. 13, p. 168.

16. Goodman, *op. cit.,* p. 14.

17. Gardner, John W., Secretary of Health, Education and Welfare, "Report on a Review and Evaluation of the Public Health Service Epidemiological Study," August 1967, submitted for the record, "Radiation Exposure of Uranium Miners," *Hearings,* Subcommittee on Research Development and Radiation, JCAE, May 9 to August 10, 1967, Part 2, p. 1261. This review corrected earlier Public

Health Service evidence that the standard recommended by the Federal Radiation Council would result in a doubling of lung cancer rates in miners. The review concluded, however, that "association of excess mortality from lung cancer . . . with estimated exposure of 800 CWLM [cumulative working level months] and above is evident. A demonstrable relationship can be inferred to exist as low as an exposure range of 100 to 400 CWLM." The standard adopted, 1 WL (working level) could be expected to result in exposures of 100 to 400 CWLM. See p. 1269.

18. "Disposition and Control of Uranium Mill Tailings Piles in the Colorado River Basin," U.S. Department of Health, Education and Welfare, Federal Water Pollution Control Administration, Region VIII, Denver, Colorado, March, 1966.

19. "Radioactive Water Pollution in the Colorado River Basin," *Hearing*, Subcommittee on Air and Water Pollution, U.S. Senate, May 5, 1966.

20. FWPCA, March 1966, *op. cit.*   ,

21. Lieberman, Joseph A. and Walter G. Belter, "Waste Management and Environmental Aspects of Nuclear Power," *Environmental Science and Technology*, Vol. 1, No. 6 (June 1967), p. 474.

22. *Ibid.*

23. Knapp, Harold A., "Cost and Safety Considerations in the Transport of Radioactive Materials," *Proceedings*, AEC and Contractor Safety and Fire Protection Conference, Germantown, Md., June 24–25, 1958, AEC Technical Information Service TID-7569, p. 54.

24. Calder, Ritchie, *Living With The Atom* (Chicago, University of Chicago Press, 1962), p. 230.

25. Knapp, *op. cit.*, p. 62.

26. Morgan, J. M., Jr., informal remarks in *Summary Report*, AEC Symposium on Packaging and Regulatory Standards for Shipping Radioactive Material, Germantown, Md., December 3–5, 1962, TID-7651, AEC Division of Technical Information Extension.

27. Patterson, D. E., "Types and Quantities of Materials Being Shipped and AEC Accident Experience," *Summary Report*, p. 3.

28. Smets, Henri B., "Review of Nuclear Accidents," *Progress in Nuclear Energy*, Series X, Law and Administration, Vol. 3, Jerry L. Weinstein (ed.), *Nuclear Liability* (New York, Pergamon Press Inc., the MacMillan Company, 1962), p. 118.

CHAPTER VII

1. Second Annual Convention, New Mexico State AFL-CIO, October 26, 1957 (mimeographed), p. 9.
2. Power Reactor Development Company v. International Union of Electrical Radio and Machine Workers, AFL-CIO, et al., 367 U.S. 396.
3. *U.S. Uranium Reserves — A Report by the Committee on Mining and Milling,* Atomic Industrial Forum, Inc., New York, August, 1966, p. 7.
4. *AEC Research Development Report, Fast Reactor Control and Safety Meeting,* November 10, 1954, AEC Technical Service. Extension, APDA-105 (declassified), 1956, p. 109.
5. *Ibid.,* p. 169.
6. *The Technology of Nuclear Reactor Safety,* Vol. I, "Reactor Physics and Control," T. J. Thompson and J. G. Beckerley (eds.), p. 631.
7. The account given of the October 5 accident is based on AEC Docket No. 50-16 "Preliminary Report on Fuel Damage in Fermi Reactor," October 11, 1966; "Investigation of the Fuel Melting Accident at the Enrico Fermi Atomic Power Plant," J. G. Duffy, W. H. Jens, J. G. Feldes, K. P. Johnson, and W. J. McCarthy, Jr., National Topical Meeting, American Nuclear Society, San Francisco, April 1967; and on additional remarks made by W. J. McCarthy, Jr., while delivering the latter paper.
8. At the April American Nuclear Society meeting.
9. McCarthy, Walter J., Jr. and Wayne H. Jens, "Enrico Fermi Fast Breeder Reactor," *Nuclear News,* November, 1967, p. 54.
10. *A Report on the Possible Effects on the Surrounding Population of an Assumed Release of Fission Products into the Atmosphere from a 300 Megawatt Nuclear Reactor Located at Lagoona Beach, Michigan,* Engineering Research Institute, University of Michigan, AEC Document number APDA-120, July 1957.
11. AEC Docket No. 50-16, Revised License Application, Enrico Fermi Atomic Power Plant, *Technical Information and Hazards Summary Report,* Vol. 7, Section VI, September 13, 1961, AEC Public Document Room, Washington, D.C.
12. National Topical Meeting, Fast Reactors, American Nuclear Society, San Francisco, April 1967.
13. "The 1967 Supplement to the 1962 Report to the President on Civilian Nuclear Power," AEC, February, 1967, p. 49.

14. Congressman Craig Hosmer, "Running with the Breeder Ball," *Nucleonics,* January 1967, p. 5.
15. Johnson, Wilfred E., Commissioner, USAEC, "Some Implications of the Fast Reactor Program in the United States," April 10, 1967, AEC Press Release No. 5-12-67.
16. "1967 Supplement," p. v.
17. *Ibid.,* p. xvi.
18. *Ibid.,* p. xvii.
19. Teller, Edward, "Fast Reactors: Maybe," *Nuclear News,* August 1967, p. 21.
20. *The Technology of Reactor Safety,* p. 600.

CHAPTER VIII

1. Jevons, W. Stanley, *The Coal Question,* first edition 1865, reprinted by Augustus M. Kelley, New York, 1965, p. 274 (quotation italicized in original).
2. Requa, M. L., 1916, quoted in Raybrawls, Arthur L., *The Energy Resources of the United States* (Washington, D.C., Catholic University of America, 1932), p. 75.
3. Putnam, Palmer Cosslett, *Energy in the Future* (New York, D. Van Nostrand Co., Inc., 1953), p. 252.
4. *Ibid.*
5. AEC, *Civilian Nuclear Power, a Report to the President — 1962,* Oak Ridge, 1962, p. 18.
6. U.S. Gov. Printing Office, Washington, D.C., 1964.
7. *Energy R&D and National Progress: Findings and Conclusions,* an Inderdepartmental Study, U.S. Gov. Printing Office, September, 1966.
8. *Ibid.,* table on p. 5
9. Jevons, *op. cit.,* p. 11 (italicized in original).
10. Hochschild, Adam, "Teapot Dome 1967?" *Ramparts,* May 1967, p. 10.
11. Lilienthal, David E., *The Journals of David E. Lilienthal,* Vol. II, *The Atomic Energy Years 1945–1950,* (New York, Harper and Row, 1964).
12. O'Brien, Brice, National Coal Association, memorandum dated August 7, 1967, Washington, D.C.
13. *Nucleonics Week,* January 18, 1968.
14. Slansky, Cyril M., "Waste Management in Close-Coupled Nuclear Fuel Cycles," *Proceedings,* Symposium on the Solidification and Long-Term Storage of Highly Radioactive Wastes, February 14–18, 1966, Richland, Washington. AEC, CONF-660208, November, 1966.

15. Orlans, Harold, *Contracting for Atoms*, Brookings Institution, Washington, D.C., 1967, p. 47.
16. *Electrical World*, August 14, 1967, p. 12.
17. Green, Harold and Alan Rosenthal, *The Government of the Atom*, (New York, Atherton Press, 1967), pp. viii-ix.

CHAPTER IX

1. Commoner, Barry, unpublished speech, 1962.

INDEX